Teaching Primary Maths

Anne Bates BA Ed (Hons) HMS.

Teaching Matters

General Editors: Sydney Hill and Colin Reid

# Teaching Primary Maths

by

**Ruth Merttens**

Senior Lecturer in Maths Education, Polytechnic of North London
and co-ordinator of the IMPACT Project

Hodder & Stoughton

A MEMBER OF THE HODDER HEADLINE GROUP

*Acknowledgements*

This book could not have been written without a great deal of help and support from those with whom I work. I would like to thank all the staff at Fleet Primary School, and especially Kate Frood, my friend and work-mate, out of discussions with whom came so many ideas. I would also like to thank my colleagues in the Teaching Studies Department, PNL, and particularly Maggy Garton, from whom I have learned so much, Alistair Ross, David Coulby and Jeff Vass, whose support, comments and advice have been much appreciated throughout the writing of this book.

I owe the deepest thanks to my husband whose patience and typing has made the whole book a reality.



*British Library Cataloguing in Publication Data*
Merttens, Ruth
Teaching primary maths.—(Teaching matters)
1. Mathematics – study and teaching (Elementary)
I. Title II. Series
372.7′3044 QA135.5
ISBN 0 7131 8469 8

First published 1987
Impression number 15 14 13 12 11 10 9 8
Year 1998 1997 1996 1995



Printed in Great Britain for Hodder & Stoughton Educational, a division of Hodder Headline Plc, 338 Euston Road, London NW1 3BH by Athenæum Press Ltd, Gateshead, Tyne & Wear

# General Editors' Preface

The books in this series provide information and advice on a wide range of educational issues for teachers who are busy, yet who are concerned to keep abreast of new developments.

The aim is practicality: slim volumes that are sources of authoritative help and swift reference, written and edited by people whose expertise in their field is backed up by experience of the everyday realities of school and classroom. The books are planned to cover well-defined topics relevant to schools in widely differing situations: subject teaching, curriculum development, areas of responsibility within schools, and the relationship of the school to the community. They are published at a time when there is a growing call for increased professional accountability in our primary and secondary schools. The 'in-service between covers' that characterizes these handbooks is designed to contribute to the vitality and development of schools and of the individuals within them.

This volume comes at a time when there is increasing pressure on teachers to adopt the approaches to mathematics which were outlined in both the Cockcroft Report and in the Curriculum Matters No. 3, HMI document. This involves teachers in practical work and the use of structural apparatus all the way throughout the primary classroom, and hopefully beyond and into secondary school. It also involves the teacher setting up problems for the children to solve and these will almost inevitably not fall under the traditional subject specialist headings. At a time when most teachers could be forgiven a mild state of panic over their own school mathematics curriculum, and also when, in most parts of the country, more money is being spent on this particular area of the curriculum, this book is designed to provide an oasis of peace.

Teachers of all years and all subjects in primary schools will find here a wealth of practical guidance and detail. Head teachers and others responsible for curricular policy will find the book a useful addition to the staff-room shelves, where it can either complement the school's use of a particular commercial mathematics scheme or provide a resource for developing a school mathematics curriculum. The book will also make an excellent introduction to primary mathematics, and will therefore enable students on ITT courses to gain immensely from its use.

**Dedication**

This book is dedicated to my father, to whom I owe so much. Also to Ian and my children, Harry, Hilda, Fred, Annie and Wilf.

# Contents

# 1

# Introduction

This book sets out to consider how best to teach mathematics in the primary school. It is a practical book, designed to assist and enthuse the teacher who is engaged in this process and to inform the student. It is not a mathematics textbook, neither is it a discussion document about cognitive theories of mathematical development.

The book is concerned to give teachers both explanations and ideas which have direct relevance to the classroom. It assumes a minimum of formal mathematical training and takes as its starting point the teacher's desire to present mathematics clearly, practically and enjoyably to the children.

The subject matter of the book is the primary mathematics curriculum and all the main topic areas within this are covered. The book complements the commercial and individual schemes used in schools by suggesting activities in each topic which enrich and expand any formal mathematics done in textbooks. However, the mathematical context of the book is also sufficiently comprehensive to enable teachers to use it as the principal source of structure, content and activities in primary mathematics.

The book relies heavily upon the approaches to the teaching of mathematics outlined in the Cockcroft Report (1982) and in the HMI Document, Curriculum Matters No. 3, *Mathematics from 5 to 16*. It advocates the use of practical activities and, moreover, that mathematics should be taught in context where at all possible. It also assumes that 'the ability to solve problems is at the heart of mathematics' (Cockcroft Report, paragraph 249) and therefore that the use of problem-solving and investigative techniques form an important part of the teaching of mathematics today.

Following these recommendations, this book advocates that we should teach mathematics in such a way that it is relevant, practical and enjoyable. For the subject to have the relevance demanded here it must be taught in as integrated a fashion as possible. Thus, the Cockcroft Report points out that: 'The experiences of young children do not come in separate packages with subject labels; as children explore the world around them, mathematical opportunities present themselves alongside others. The teacher needs, therefore, to seek opportunities for drawing mathematical experiences out of a wide range of children's activities. Very many curricular areas give rise to mathematics.' (paragraph 325). This relates to the experience of most teachers that, when children are taught a skill out of context, it is not easy to teach the skill, hard for the children to memorize it, and often difficult for them to transfer the skill to contexts other than the one in which it was first presented.

The subject must be taught as far as possible through the use of practical activities. Educationalists and advisors have been saying this for so long that it is hard to understand why there is still so great a concentration on formal arithmetic of the paper and pencil sort. The HMI Document sees practical activity in mathematics as falling into three main categories:

1) Practical work which is done to assist the acquisition of a concept. For example, the use of Cuisenaire Rods to demonstrate the difference between two numbers.
2) Practical work which is an integral part of the activity or topic. For example, filling a teapot with 18 egg-cupfuls of water in order to measure its capacity.
3) Practical work which is used as one of many strategies towards solving a problem. For example, to find all the square numbers up to 100, it may be easiest for a small child to build them out of Multilink.

For children to learn mathematics in such a way that they are confident in the subject, that they enjoy it and that they can use the skills they acquire within the classroom outside its boundaries, it is essential that as many connections as possible are made between the mathematics learnt in class and ordinary everyday situations. Only if children are allowed to learn mathematics as far as possible in the same way that they learn everything else, by using it to solve problems, can the subject have the relevance which its proper place demands. Thus, from the very early stages, children should be encouraged to make explicit connections between the mathematics they learn in class and things that they do outside the classroom which do not feel like maths at all. This helps them to knit their mathematical learning experiences together into one coherent whole.

In solving problems, children have to:

1) learn to work co-operatively, to listen to what other people are saying, and to be able to offer ideas of their own;
2) develop strategies, experiment, try out ideas and test theories;
3) use skills learned and concepts acquired within a context so that the relevance and usefulness of those skills is perceived and the children's grasp of them is reinforced.

Children are on the whole motivated to solve problems. Finding a solution is intrinsically satisfying and the fact that it is not necessarily the same as someone else's solution is a bonus. Also, solving problems is something which children, like adults, are doing much of the time, whether the problem is getting a toy which is out of reach, or planning a two-week holiday on a shoestring budget. Solving problems is not merely a classroom activity – it is part of life!

This book is about the teaching and learning of mathematics. It contains plenty of 'tips for teachers', but it also assumes a particular approach to mathematics which will underpin every activity the teacher does and every topic or project that s/he plans. It will help those teachers for whom mathematics was a bad memory at school or college and those students who are struggling to come to grips with how to teach it. It is written against a background of experience of both mathematics and the primary classroom, in the firm conviction that if we can only allow children to discover, explore and enjoy mathematics, we will have gone some way toward making accessible a beautiful and fascinating subject.

# 2

# Sets and sorting

When small children arrive at school, they have already come into contact with the notion of a set, having played with train sets, tea sets, Lego sets and so on. So we can start with the idea of a set as a 'group of things which belong together'. This idea can then be developed by sorting things into sets and their 'complements', that is, things in a set and things not in it (Figure 1). The concept of a set, then, is a basic one in mathematics and it recurs throughout all the mathematics which the children subsequently study. It is linked inextricably with the concept of sorting.

Figure 1

## Sorting

Sorting can be an under-rated activity in infant classes. Sometimes it is assumed that children can already sort, and often it is not clear what is being achieved through giving children practice in sorting. However, being able to sort and to classify is an absolutely essential skill. The sorting, classification and ordering of information forms the basis for all knowledge. Those children who have difficulty sorting and organizing are at an increasing disadvantage as they progress through the school system.

## Attribute cards

Attribute cards consist of a pack of 25 to 30 different cards which may be pictures of any set of objects differing only in particular attributes. For example, they could consist of pictures of cats; some with a tail showing, some without; some with whiskers, some without; some ginger, some black; (Figure 2). This allows the cards to be sorted in various ways according to different criteria. A set or two of attribute cards is a wonderful resource for any teacher to make and keep. They can be used in so many different ways throughout the primary school. Some ideas include:

Figure 2

### Guessing and sorting games

One child or a pair of children sort the attribute cards into two or more sets. The other children in the group must attempt to guess what are the criteria for belonging to those sets. For example it might be cats with tails and cats without.

This game can be extended and made more complex for top infants and juniors by using cards with more than three attributes. A set of flags does very well in this connection since flags have so many attributes that it can become quite difficult to guess the reason for a particular partition into sets. A pack of ordinary playing cards also makes a good set of attribute cards for slightly older children. With infants, it is a good idea to use actual objects, such as buttons, badges or dominoes as a change from the attribute cards.

**Card games**

Many ordinary card games can be adapted very successfully for use with attribute cards. A version of 'snap' can be played where the children may only call out 'snap' if the two cards being compared differ in only one attribute. So, a player could call 'snap' if the card that was turned up was a ginger cat with a tail and whiskers and it was being matched with a black cat with a tail and whiskers.

Similarly, a memory game (pelmanism) can be played where all the cards are laid out face down and the children take it in turns to turn over a pair. If their pair differs by only one attribute, they may keep it, otherwise they must turn the pair back face-down. The one with the most pairs at the end wins.

**Attribute dominoes**

This is a version of dominoes which can be played with two, three or four players, depending upon how many attribute cards there are. A few cards are dealt to each player. The players take it in turns to play and the aim is to be the first to possess no cards. The first player places a card, like a domino, in the middle of the table. The second player must place another card next to the first card, but the card they place must differ from the first placed card by exactly two attributes. Players go on adding cards to the line, at either end, in such a way that each adjacent card will differ from its neighbour in exactly two attributes. The first person who has no cards left wins.

Attribute cards can provide an immense source of fun for the children, who can sort them, organize them and sometimes put the cards into overlapping or intersecting sets. Through the use of these cards, children can develop and use the concept of a set and its complements. Often the cards can be one of the most popular resources in the classroom.

There are many other resources which can be used to develop similar activities to those outlined above. Children often collect things – cards, stamps, flags, buttons, foreign coins and an almost infinite variety of other objects, all of which can be used in this way.

## Sets and complements

Most early work with children concentrates on things belonging and not belonging to particular sets. A variety of ideas can be used in this connection. Children can be asked to point out the 'odd-one-out' in a group or picture of objects. In isolating the 'thing which shouldn't be there', the children will have to decide what constitutes a description of the set of things which are being considered. Their decision about this may be unspoken and intuitive to start with, but they can then be asked to justify their choice of the 'odd-one-out' and this will make them verbalize the criteria for the membership of the set, and therefore move towards an explicit definition. An example of this type of process is provided by some children looking at a group of toys consisting of a rabbit, a bird, a doll, a bear, a brick, a plastic fish, and a 'Snoopy'. Each of the children might isolate the odd-one-out differently: one might distinguish the fish, another the brick, yet another the 'Snoopy', and a fourth the doll. The first child would then have to explain why the object isolated had been selected (because it was the only toy which belonged in the bath). Thus for that child the definition of the set is 'toys which do not belong in the bath'. But each of the others may have a different definition in mind, and they too can be asked to account for their choice. Such an account must contain an implicit definition of the set with which they are dealing. The older the children, the more they can be asked to make that definition explicit and to put it into words.

Another useful method of helping children to verbalize the reasons for their classifications is to ask them to find and select ten small objects from around the classroom and to sort them into two piles. They must then explain the reasons for their partitioning. If several children collect ten small objects, the teacher will then have enough things to encourage a joint sorting process which could result in several sets (things made of wood/paper, things made of plastic, things made of fabric, and other things). In this connection, it might be necessary to introduce the idea of overlapping sets, since something could be in more than one set at once by virtue of its being made from wood and plastic.

## Intersection and union

The idea that something can be in more than one set at once can

*Children can sort in a variety of ways*

prove difficult for small children to take on board. We can help by using large plastic hoops on the floor and deciding to sort things into them as separate sets. For example, one hoop could contain red things and the other hoop could contain things made of wood. The children are then faced with the problem of what to do with a red wooden brick. The suggestion to overlap one hoop over another so that the brick can be placed inside both the hoops at once may come from the children themselves or it might need to come from the teacher. The children can be encouraged to talk about which objects are in the overlap of the two hoops and some teachers and commercial schemes introduce the word 'intersection'. However, this cannot be seen as essential and perhaps not even as advisable, especially with children who find long words or 'mathematical terminology' off-putting or intimidating.

The idea of the union of two sets as containing all the things in those two sets together is one which children may acquire implicitly without necessarily being able to use the associated terminology. Thus, if we have the sets of those children who have dogs, those who have cats, those who have budgies, etc., they may understand very well that all the children named in those sets have pets.

Practical activities such as this, where one object cannot be in two separated hoops at the same time, form the basis for the introduction of Venn diagrams.

## Venn diagrams

(*i*) Venn diagrams provide a very useful form of graphical representation. Sometimes the information to be displayed, because of its very nature, is not suitable for a block graph. An example might be the ways in which the children in the class come to school. Suppose that, in a survey, 26 children were found to walk to school, one to come by car, one by bike, and one by train. A block graph will be useless here since it will simply look like one long column with three small blocks along the x-axis. Using a Venn diagram, it is possible to display the information more attractively by varying the size of the sets to fit the data, since there is no question of scale. Another example is the months of the year in which the children were born. This information is far better expressed as a Venn diagram with a series of sets on the wall (Figure 3) to avoid an immensely long x-axis with a smattering of blocks along it. Of course, the choice of how best to display information should, where possible, be a matter for negotiation and discussion with the children. In this way they come to see graphical representation, like words, as a powerful means of communication.

Figure 3

(*ii*) Another advantage of this type of pictorial representation is that each child's name appears only once, whereas on a block graph displaying the same information, the same name may well be represented three times (Figure 4). This can be very confusing for the children. With Venn diagrams, as with all pictorial representation, the display is only ever as good as the questions asked about it.

Sometimes a complex Venn diagram may demand a lot of thinking about if sense is to be made of some of the finer points of the information being displayed. Thus, in the above example, if we asked which girl likes Coca Cola and milk but not juice, many children would puzzle over it, while some of the and more experienced children would have no problem at all.

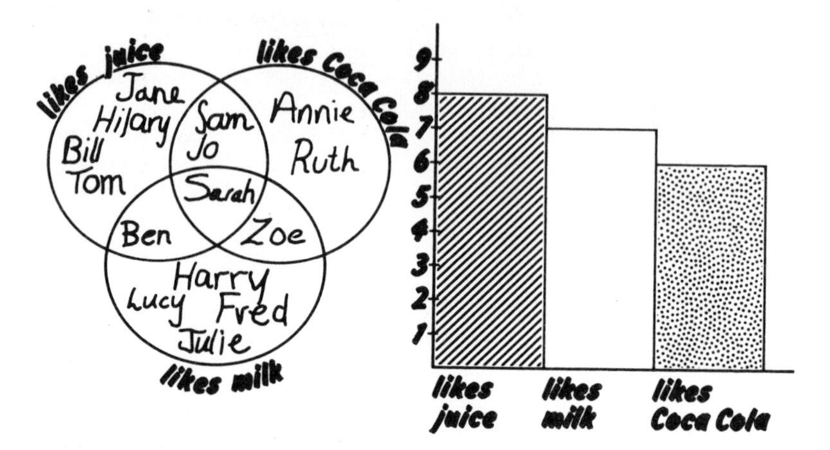


Figure 4

(*iii*) Venn diagrams can be used as a way of giving skills practice an added twist (Figure 5). Requiring that particular types of numbers be placed in specified related sets makes an interesting task for junior children. Later on the children can be encouraged to think in terms of the intersection and union of two sets (Figure 6) and they can be asked what numbers were in the union of the two sets, what were in the intersection, and maybe what numbers were not in either of the two sets (complement).

(*iv*) Children can happily create their own Venn diagrams from their own data. For example, if children have obtained the following information about their class:

| *Has for breakfast* | *Number of children* |
|---|---:|
| cereal | 25 |
| bread or toast | 19 |
| bacon, egg etc. | 12 |
| other | 3 |

they can then be asked to depict this on a Venn diagram. This process is a very useful one as it is essential that children do not get the idea that statistical presentations of any sort come ready made. They have to be created by someone and are therefore as much open to abuse as are words.

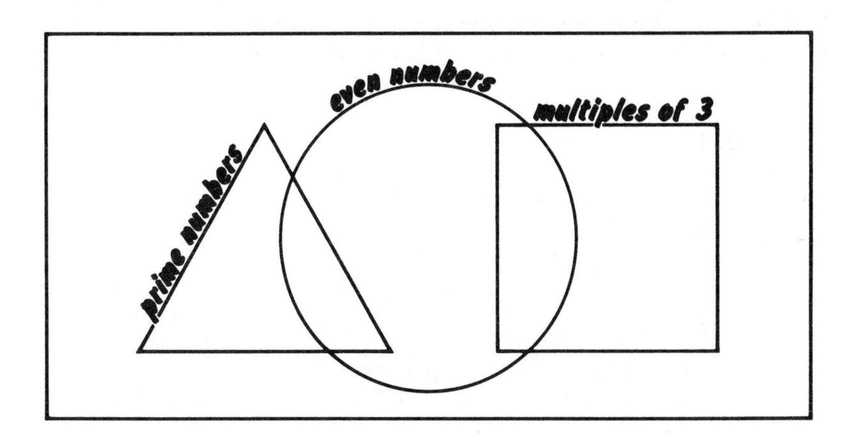


Figure 5

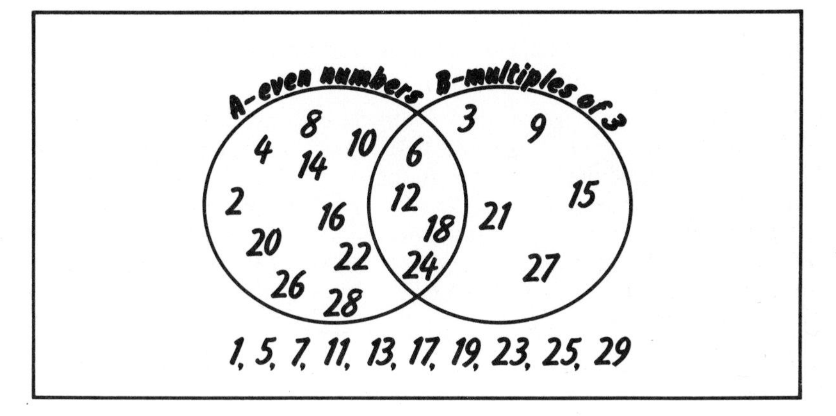


Figure 6

## Set notation

The use of this is often stressed far too much at the expense of the practical experiences of sorting and information classification which are so essential in this area of mathematics. Unless it is needed for some specific assessment purpose, the notation of set theory can safely be left to the secondary schools.

## Matching equivalent sets

Many commercial maths schemes introduce number through the medium of set theory and matching. Children are capable of matching two sets – one object against another. The understanding of difference as the basis of an unequal comparison arises when small children match sets one-to-one in an attempt to find out which has more members. Thus, if two children are given unequal numbers of sweets on a plate, even before they can count the one who has fewer will protest.

When one set can be matched one-to-one on to another, we say that they are equivalent sets (Figure 7). Developing this concept of equivalence is important since it forms the basis of much of the number work and other mathematics to be studied later on. Children can come to realize that it is not necessary to count the members of a set to prove that they are equivalent; this can be established by matching one set on to another. There is plenty of practice to be found in the primary classroom in matching one-to-one (coats to pegs, straws to milk bottles, etc.). Children can also gain experience in matching two-to-one and three-to-one and so on, for example, shoes to children, books to trays.

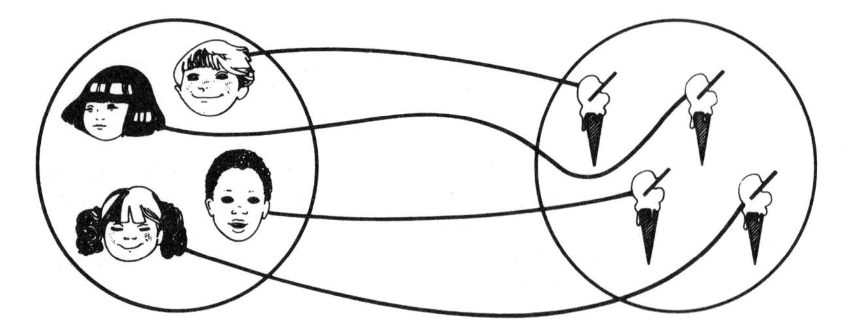

Figure 7

## Relations

Relations occur between the members of sets. Children meet relations in all sorts of circumstances. Some common ones include: Fred is the brother of Annie, Hilda is the sister of Harry, Matthew is taller than Fred, Annie likes Hilda, Harry plays with Jeff. We can see that:

is the brother of
is the sister of
likes
plays with
is taller than

are different sorts of relation and can be depicted on a Venn diagram (Figure 8).

Later on, children will use more abstract relations to form the basis of functions. Thus 'doubling' might be a relation between two sets of numbers.

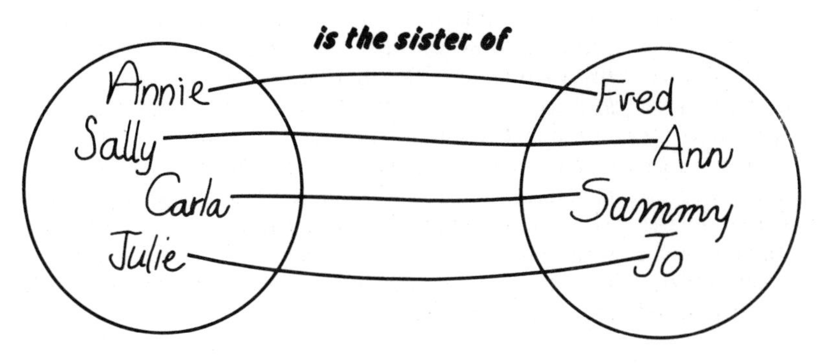


Figure 8

## Conclusion

The ideas of set theory form the basis of much mathematics, but they are also useful in other curriculum areas. Since the concepts involved are so important, the use of practical activities is particularly crucial so that children are able to acquire these ideas and to formulate for themselves the relations between them.

# 3

# Early number

We are so used to dealing with numbers that it is sometimes difficult for us to imagine what it is like not to understand how they work and what they are. In actual fact, numbers are used in several different ways and to serve two quite distinct purposes. They can be sets or they can be used to order things. It is helpful to start with the experiences which small children have of numbers.

## How do we first meet numbers?

Children first meet numbers in the following circumstances:

as names
as sets
as 'counting'

### As names

Numbers are frequently used to 'name' one thing and thereby distinguish it from other similar objects. For example, we number houses in a street, flats in a block, buses. If we say we live in Flat No. 68 we are 'naming' our flat; we could equally well say we lived at 'Fred flat' or at 'Flat A'; flats are often named by letters rather than numbers. Indeed houses are very often named: Rose Cottage, Chez Nous, Kenwood House, and so on. If a child tells us s/he catches the 'one-four-five' to school, she is naming a particular bus and she has no concept of the number 145 *per se*.

### As sets

Children learn early to recognize the concept of 'difference.' If I put 5 Smarties on Tom's plate and 3 on Ann's plate, then, from the age of 20 months or so, Ann will shriek. Such a recognition of 'difference', the idea 'It's not fair!', often precedes the acquisiton of the words to express it. Of course the small child is not counting. S/he is, presumably, performing a matching operation and recognizing the non-equivalence of the sets. In fact, meeting numbers as sets – 'There are 5 mugs on the table', 'I have 3 sweets' – is a common experience for young children. These are 'cardinal numbers'.

It is important to remember that cardinal numbers are sets. They tell us the number of members in a set: how many sweets on the plate or mugs on the table. When I say 'There are 5 mugs of beer on the table', I mean that there are 5 mugs of beer on the table at the same time, *not* that there is one mug on the table now, there will be another in an hour, and so on.

### As 'counting'

Children also meet numbers in counting situations:

– in rhymes:
*One, two, three, four, five,*
*Once I caught a fish alive.*
*Six, seven, eight, nine, ten,*
*Then I let it go again.*

– on the stairs
(which should really be counted 'first, second, third . . .)

– in dressing
*One sock, two socks.*
*One button, two buttons, three buttons . . .*

There are other circumstances in which small children meet numbers. They hear people telling the time and referring to children's ages. Telephone numbers are a sort of 'code'. But the children's main uses of numbers in the pre-school years will be as names, as sets and in counting.

There are also, of course, ordinal numbers (*first, second, third, etc*). They are used to indicate the place of an object, event or activity, in a line or series: She came first in the race; I will meet you on the second day of the holiday; It is the fourth shop on the left.

### The inherent contradiction

Cardinal numbers depend on things being in a set all at the same time. There are 4 mugs on the table now, but in order to find out how many, we must count. And counting means ordering things. This problem is inherent in the concept of number itself.

Small children are occasionally very disturbed by this and will wonder, having counted a line of objects, picking up each one in turn: 'Why am I holding one thing and saying six?' There is here a realization of the difference between cardinal and ordinal numbers.

It is interesting to note that so different is the concept of cardinal numbers from that of ordinal numbers that nearly all languages reflect this by having words with different etymological roots for the numbers one, two . . . and the numbers first, second . . . Language here reflects the difference between the underlying concepts.

## Counting

Children must indeed learn to count but it is difficult to assess their progress for the following reasons:

(*i*) Counting does not simply consist of chanting the numbers in order. Many children come into school able to 'count' to 20 or even above without any idea of what they are doing. Being able to recite the numbers as a sort of rhyme gives no indication of the child's understanding of number.

(*ii*) Children must come to develop an idea of the 'size' of different numbers. They have to be able to visualize what eight beads looks and feels like, and what eight people looks like. They have to realize that number is dependent on quantity and not on volume. So it is easy to make a collection of 100 marbles in the class while 100 bricks is more difficult to collect. Getting this sort of feel for number is a result of handling sets of objects, estimating how many, then checking the estimate. Children can build models from Lego or Multilink, estimate how many pieces they have used and then count to check. They can thread a string of beads and do the same or draw a pattern on squared or isometric paper, estimate the number of coloured squares or triangles and then count them. All these ways of handling numbers of objects help to develop a sense of number which forms an essential foundation for any future work.

Children can then be encouraged to create patterns out of specific numbers. Thus 5 counters can be arranged in various ways besides the traditional way (Figure 1).

Patterns, or arrays, have several values. Besides developing a sense of the 'fiveness' of 5, they are also part of a useful technique for counting efficiently and they help develop the skills necessary to distinguish some numbers from others, for example, even and odd numbers.

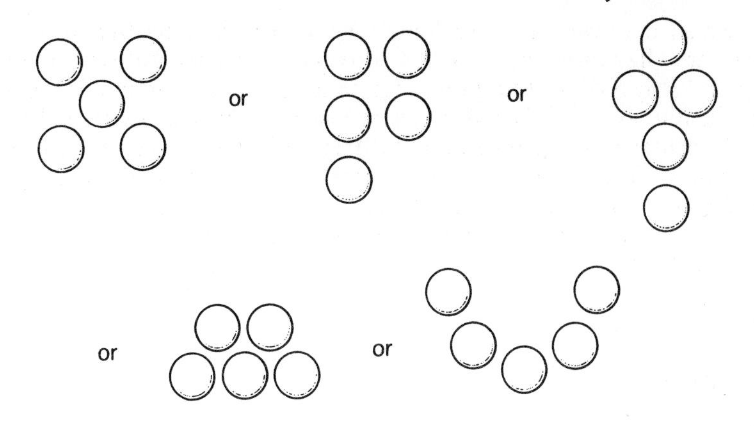


Figure 1

(*iii*) Learning to count a number of objects efficiently is a different process entirely from simply being able to count. It is all too common a sight to watch small children counting a set of objects inefficiently, not touching each one as they go or forming them into any sensible order so as to distinguish the counted from the uncounted – and making a mistake as a result. Most errors in traditional addition sums performed by counting out sets of beads and adding them are not errors of addition but errors of counting.

Children must both sort and order as they count. They need to move the objects around as they count them so that they form an array or a pattern. In this way they can check their figures at a quick glance (Figure 2).

## Grouping and tallying numbers

In time the children will develop the ability to count in groups. They will first group their counters as they count and gradually cease to say every number on counting but mark only the multiples of the group – two, four, six, eight . . . The advantages of developing this method of counting are obvious. It leads almost automatically into the even-odd distinction, into multiplication and factors. It is also the natural beginning to 'place value' work.

Learning to group numbers and then to 'exchange' is necessary in order to develop the idea of place value. Children can be encouraged to group things as they count and, where it is natural to do so, exchange them: for example, in counting eggs, 9 eggs can be grouped as 1 box and 3 eggs.

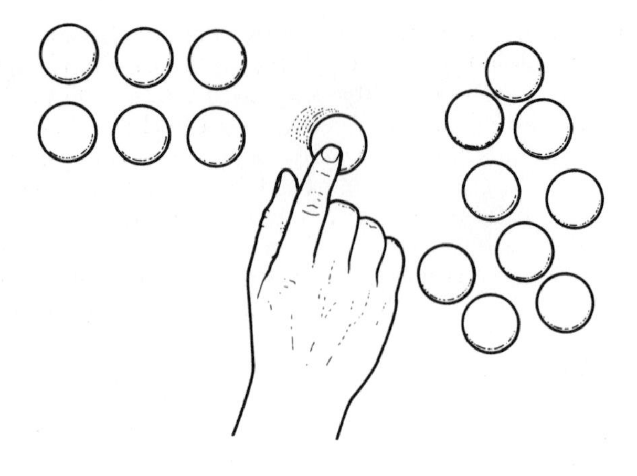

Figure 2

When counting large numbers of things, children can begin to tally in various ways (Figure 3). This is particularly useful if they need to count things which are moving, such as cars in a traffic survey where they will need to make marks on paper for every vehicle seen. However, since counting in tens or fives is too sophisticated a skill for very small children, even when they have grouped and arranged the objects or tallied the marks on a page, they usually need assistance in the final count to help them manage it accurately.

It is probably best to start introducing grouping activities in the middle and top infant classes in preparation for work and computation with larger numbers.

Figure 3

## Conservation of number

One of the most basic concepts children must develop is that of 'conservation of number'. This is the idea that if I rearrange a set number of objects, the number of objects does not change. So if I set 6 plates on the table for tea and ask the child how many there are, s/he will count. If I then move the plates around the table and repeat my question it should not be necessary for the child to re-count. It must be clearly established in the child's mind that the number does not depend on the pattern in which the plates are arranged. Number is independent of arrangement in this context.

Many children will require lots of practical experience with structural apparatus and colouring patterns to grasp this concept fully.

## Number patterns

The use of structural apparatus in building numbers and forming them into patterns is invaluable in the early stages.

(*i*) Odd and even numbers. Children can be asked to build the numbers from 1 to 20 in rows of two, like a crocodile of children going on an outing. These models can then be matched to their numbers on the number line and all the ones which have a 'knob' or unpaired brick can be put in the set labelled 'odd'. The even numbers, of course, make an exact rectangle (Figure 4).

*Children getting into pairs to go out*

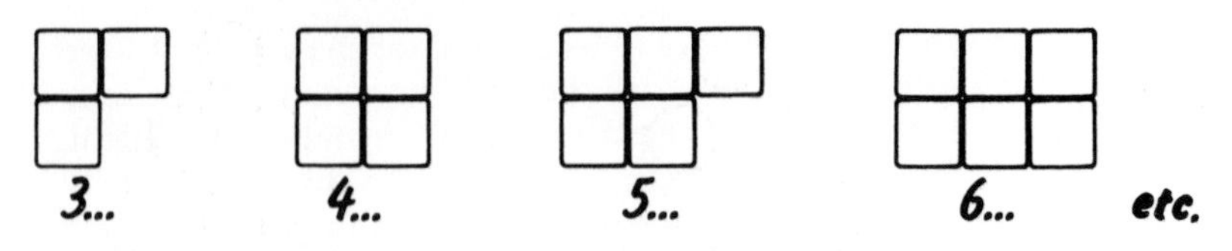


Figure 4

(*ii*) Square numbers. The children build squares out of Multilink. To start with, this activity should be set up as an investigation and the children may build open or closed squares. Later on they can be restricted to closed squares. They write down the number of cubes in each square together with its side length (Figure 5).

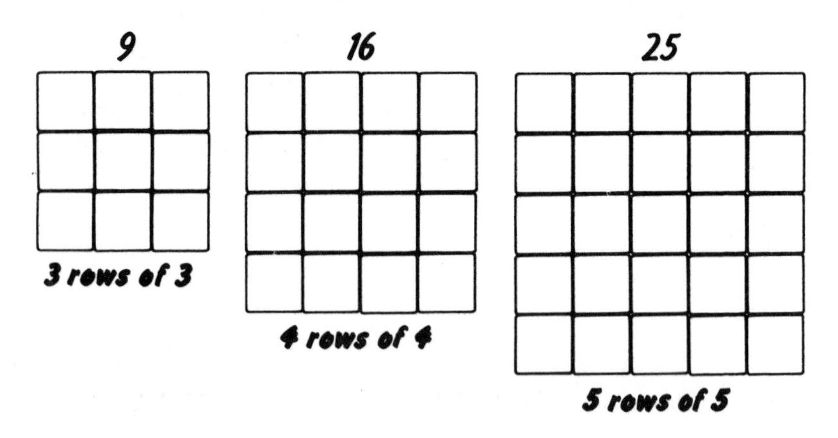


Figure 5

Square numbers are useful for later number work. They form the leading diagonal of the multiplication square and are also important for multi-base work. Later, the children can move from Multilink to colouring squared paper.

(*iii*) Triangular numbers. In the same way as they build up squares, the children can build up triangles. This time it is easiest to use round counters (Figure 6). But it is possible to use Multilink (Figure 7). The children build as many 'triangular numbers' as they can and write down the series of numbers they obtain. Then they can be encouraged to add them together, adding consecutive triangular numbers (Figure 8). Most of the children will recognize that they can obtain the square numbers this way.

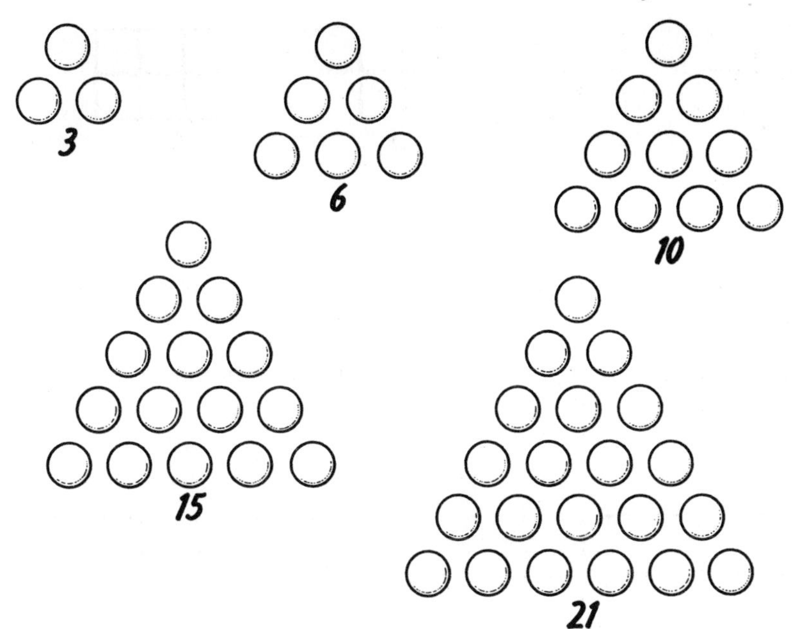


Figure 6

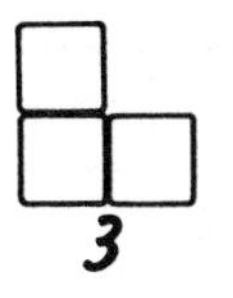


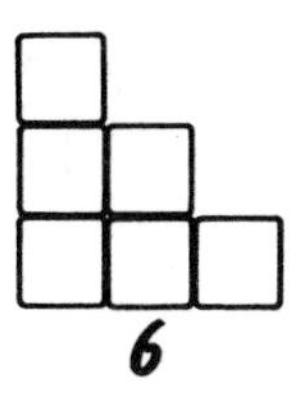


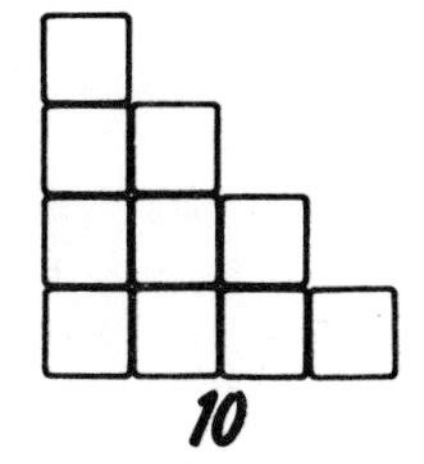


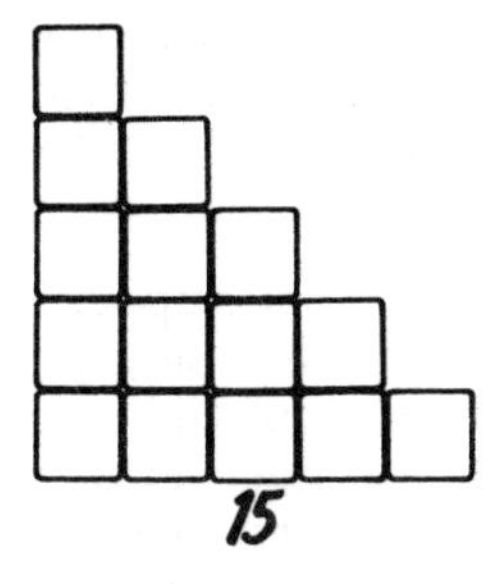


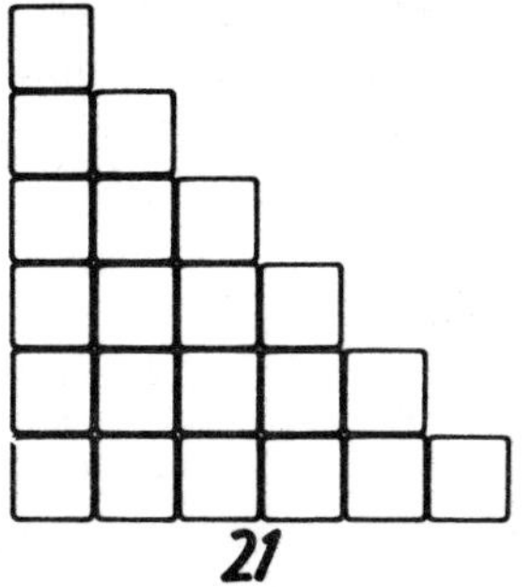


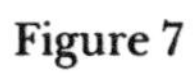

Figure 7

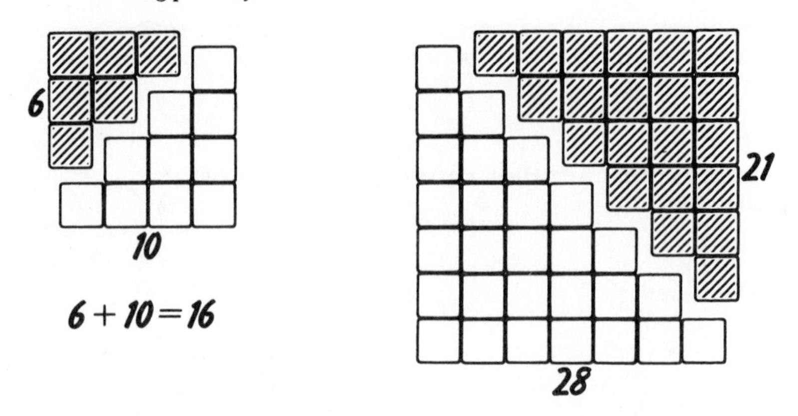


Figure 8

*(iv)* Children can also build rectangular numbers and obtain a series of numbers in this way.

*(v)* It is interesting for children to build up one square from the next and to look at the differences. The easiest way to do this is to colour squared paper (Figure 9), adding on an L-shape each time. The children will usually recognize that the differences are the odd numbers.

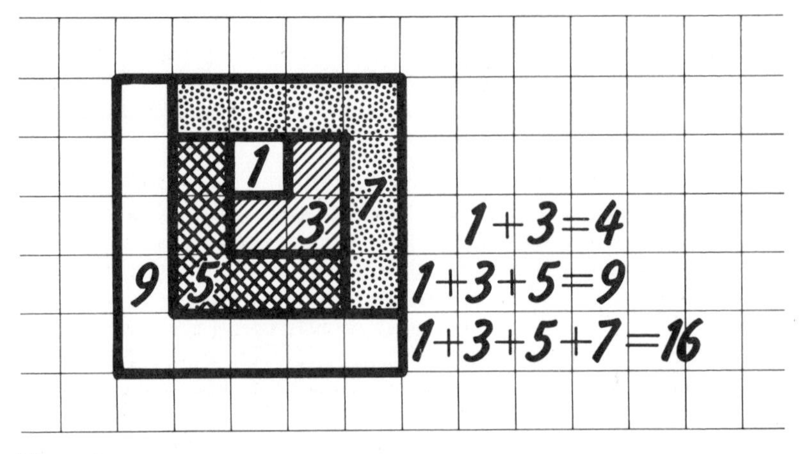


Figure 9

They can also be encouraged to discover that the difference between any two adjacent squares is the sum of their two roots. We can demonstrate this practically by breaking up an L-shape into its long and short parts. This practical exercise can be done with children from 6 to 16.

## Number lines, number squares and structural apparatus

### Number lines

Number lines can be much more than a small plastic strip pinned to the top of the table getting tattier each year. Children should make their own number line. It is important to remind them that numbers do not end, therefore the number line should indicate that the numbers go on past the last number on the line. The children can put any personal details they like on to their number lines where these are appropriate to particular numbers. For example: I have 3 sisters; My cat is 2 years' old; I am 6 years old; I live at No. 8(a). Sometimes it may be necessary to put a vital piece of information down with an arrow indicating that the number it applies to is off the edge of the paper: My Grandad is 81, he lives at No. 221(b). This helps to reinforce the idea in children's minds of numbers going on and on and of there being no end to the counting process.

Once they have made their own personal number lines the children will be more familiar with the concept of numbers forming a series or line. This activity will have strengthened the notions of ordering and succession, of one number following another and will thus have reinforced the whole idea of ordinal numbers.

Number lines can be used for a variety of purposes with small children:

(*i*) Addition as counting on. A more traditional approach to addition used counters laid under the appropriate numbers. Although this does have the advantage that it emphasizes the concept of adding as taking the union of two distinct sets, it has severe disadvantages as a method of practising addition once the concept is acquired. First, it is very slow and cumbersome and therefore boring. It is always useful to encourage children to speed up the actual process of computation as much as possible so that it does not become laborious and put them off.

Secondly, using this method children have three possibilities of error which really have nothing to do with the additon itself. They can make a mistake counting out the first number of counters, they can do the same counting out the second number of counters, and there remains the possibility that they can make the same mistake counting out the answer.

Clearly, if we have a reasonable alternative available, it is not satisfactory to teach the children such a tedious and error-prone method. And the number line itself provides the alternative. The same sum can be approached more efficiently using the number line. The child reads the sum and decides which is the larger number: this is an important step which becomes vital once we progress to mental arithmetic. It is sensible always to add a small number to a larger if possible. Once the child has isolated the larger number, s/he puts a finger on that number on the number line. The second number now tells the child how many steps to count on and the answer is read off the number line. The only possible counting error using this method would be in the counting on. The method also establishes in the child's mind both the fact that moving right along the number line leads to bigger and bigger numbers and the fact that addition can be seen as a form of 'counting on'. Both these ideas have useful applications in later graph and co-ordinate work.

(*ii*) Subtraction as counting back. The number line is not nearly as useful for subtraction as for addition. To start with, subtraction is best introduced as 'difference', which will be discussed later on. Secondly, by the time the children really begin to do subtraction as computations, they often dispense with the number line and use other structural apparatus such as Cuisenaire Rods.

However, the number line can be one of many aids to achieving an answer to subtraction sums. There are two ways of using the line. Either the child can count the number of steps between the two numbers – that is to say they can perform complementary addition by counting on from the lower number to the higher (Figure 10). Or they can count back from the higher number the number of steps indicated by the lower number. This method is the reverse of the method used for addition. The former is to be slightly preferred as it leads naturally in to 'gazuptas' or 'shopkeepers' addition'.

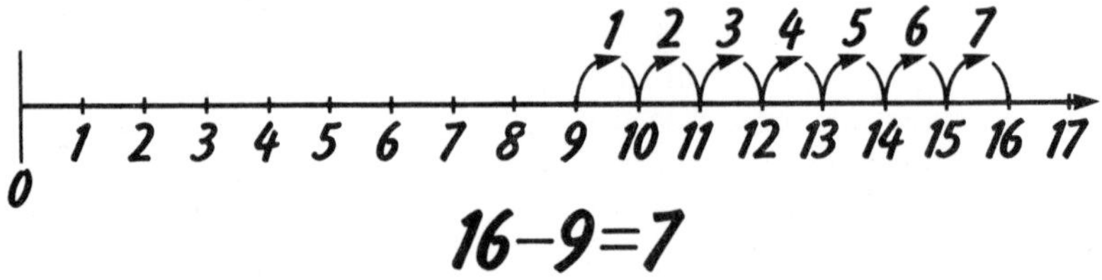

$$16-9=7$$

Figure 10

With small children for whom colouring is often tedious and something of a chore, a number square duplicated on 2 cm square paper provides an alternative way of demonstrating the patterns. Different coloured cubes of Multilink or Unifix can be used standing on the appropriate squares. So, if a red cube is placed on every even number and a yellow cube on every third number the multiples of 6 stand out very clearly.

*Children building patterns on a number square*

## Cuisenaire Rods or Colour Factor and Multilink

Cuisenaire Rods are an under-used resource in most schools. Bought in the 1960s in the wake of John Holt's book, *How Children Fail*, they have too often sat in cupboards gathering dust. In fact they are a most useful resource.

(*i*) The 'size' of numbers. A large scale number line can be laid along the table top and then each number can be built using either Cuisenaire Rods or Multilink (Figure 12). This gives a pattern of 'stairs' which provides a graphic illustration that if we add 1 to a number we get the next number in the counting sequence. This sounds obvious but there are a horrifyingly large number of children who have not understood this in the infant school.

(*iii*) Multiplication and counting in groups. At a later stage the number line can be used to develop multiplication. Different size steps can be taken along the number line and the numbers 'trodden on' can be noted. Even numbers – and odd numbers – can be isolated on the number line by counting in twos. This helps to establish 0 as an even number because it forms part of the pattern.

**Number squares**

| 0 | 1 | 2 | 3 | 4 | 5 | 6 | 7 | 8 | 9 |
|---|---|---|---|---|---|---|---|---|---|
| 10 | 11 | 12 | 13 | 14 | 15 | 16 | 17 | 18 | 19 |
| 20 | 21 | 22 | 23 | 24 | 25 | 26 | 27 | 28 | 29 |
| 30 | 31 | 32 | 33 | 34 | 35 | 36 | 37 | 38 | 39 |
| 40 | 41 | 42 | 43 | 44 | 45 | 46 | 47 | 48 | 49 |
| 50 | 51 | 52 | 53 | 54 | 55 | 56 | 57 | 58 | 59 |
| 60 | 61 | 62 | 63 | 64 | 65 | 66 | 67 | 68 | 69 |
| 70 | 71 | 72 | 73 | 74 | 75 | 76 | 77 | 78 | 79 |
| 80 | 81 | 82 | 83 | 84 | 85 | 86 | 87 | 88 | 89 |
| 90 | 91 | 92 | 93 | 94 | 95 | 96 | 97 | 98 | 99 |

Figure 11

A number square should include 0 and not start, as some commercially printed ones do, at 1. This is because if the first number is 0, the re-grouping into 2 figures takes place at the beginning of the next line – thus all the numbers on row 1 have one digit, all the numbers on row 2 begin with a 1 and so on. This avoids the clumsy configuration obtained if the square leaves off the 0. Also it is important that small children especially do not lose sight of the importance of zero. It is, of course, a place-holder but it also means a set with nothing in it.

Children can colour the even numbers on the square, thus reinforcing the 'alternate number' aspect of evenness, but also bringing out the fact that 0 is an even number. Top infants can colour every third number (count two, colour, count two, colour . . .) and get the rather pretty diagonal patterns. Later on the children can colour other multiples and get different patterns – the sevens and eights are both interesting.

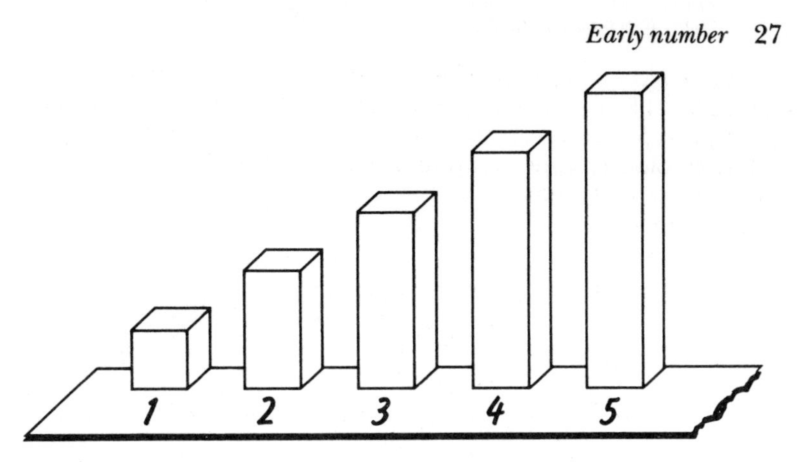


Figure 12

(*ii*) The 'difference between' two numbers. Cuisenaire Rods or Colour Factor provide an excellent way of showing the difference between two numbers. For example, 10 – 4 can be demonstrated practically using the rods (Figure 13). Once the children are used to handling the rods, the counting involved in subtraction and addition is greatly reduced, and this can be a tremendous advantage.

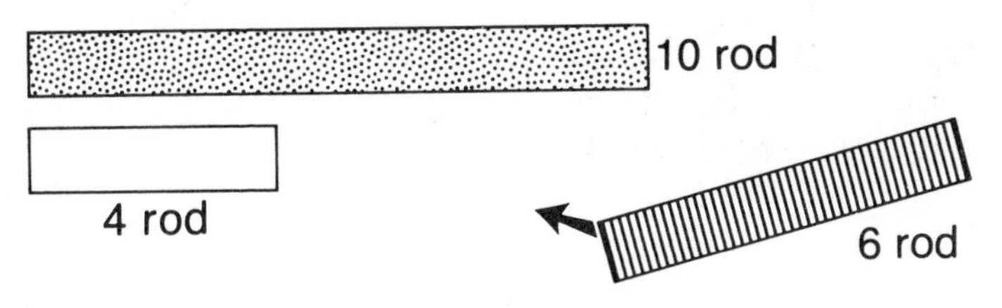


Figure 13

(*iii*) Number bonds. The rods and Multilink can similarly be used to develop an understanding of number bonds. Their structured use in this connection will be discussed under 'Number bonds' in chapter 4.

(*iv*) Making a 'train' or line of a certain length. This is a useful practical investigation with the minimum of recording necessary to achieve a result and it is best done in small groups of three or four.

Mini-investigations can be undertaken requiring the children to find different ways of making 'trains' of a specific length (Figure 14). These can be as short as 4, in which case there are only five ways:

One 4 rod
One 3 rod and one 1 rod
Two 2 rods
One 2 rod and two 1 rods
Four 1 rods

Or they can be 10 (or even 12 using Colour Factor). The ordering of information that this investigation requires provides much needed practice in self-organized mathematical thinking.

It is interesting with older children to encourage them to find a pattern so that they can predict how many ways there are of making a 17 train or a 20 train.

Figure 14

(*v*) Further work with rods. Colour Factor or Cuisenaire Rods are exceedingly useful in the following topic areas:

Fractions
Ratio and proportion
Length and area
Factors
Multiplication
Division

Their use in these areas will be covered later in this book in the appropriate chapters. However, one or two points are worth mentioning here. In the infant school Cuisenaire Rods provide an excellent introduction to working with fractions. They can be used to demonstrate halves, thirds, and quarters. Notions such as 'twice as long,' and 'three times the length', can be explored using the rods. This leads on to the general idea of doubling and trebling which can be demonstrated practically with the apparatus.

Multilink can be used to develop early ideas of volume. The children can be asked to build models in 3 dimensions, and when they have mastered this skill the tasks can be made harder by, for example, demanding 3-d models of uniform cross-section.

Numbers form a much more complex structure than we often

remember. Some of the most important concepts are acquired by children during their first two or three years at school. Practical work is once again crucial to the acquisition of many of the ideas involved in this chapter. Allowing children the time to develop a real 'feel' for numbers and an enjoyment of their properties gives them a far greater advantage later on. Too great an emphasis on skills practice or paper recording only leads to boredom and frustration. Children can 'play' with numbers and become 'friendly' with them. They should not be allowed to develop the habit of copying by rote.

# 4

# Number bonds, operations and place value

## Approaches to the teaching of number facts

The HMI Curriculum Matters document, *Mathematics from 5–16*, points out two things as regards the teaching of number facts. First, number facts and skills practice should, as far as possible, arise in context. If a child is playing a game, the numbers on a dice may be added up as a necessary part of playing that game. The addition is not done with paper and pencil but after a relatively short time the repetition means that the child ceases to calculate the answer and starts to remember it. If a 'sum' arises out of another activity, the child will frequently perform it without trouble because it is necessary to do so. Secondly, if operations like addition, subtraction, etc. are not seen in context, there is always the danger that 'sums' will have no relevance outside the classroom.

There are three reasons why it is helpful for children not to do too many pages of sums out of any context:

### Sums do not assist the memorizing of number facts

If a child can do the sums, there is little point in continuing to practise the skill. There are many more effective ways of learning addition facts than repeating addition sums. If the child cannot do such sums, a sense of repeated failure and boredom will set in.

### Sums do not help in the understanding of addition

Repeated practice does not help a child learn *how* to add up. In order to learn how, many practical experiences and much handling of structural apparatus, etc. are needed. The HMI document recommends that a variety of practical experiences are essential to the acquisition of any concepts and that plenty of time should be allowed for these.

**Sums do not enhance the enjoyment of the subject**

Children's attitudes to maths are formed early and negative attitudes are especially difficult to change. It is, therefore, imperative that the children enjoy learning mathematics as much as possible. It is important that they see it as a creative and not a dull subject. It is short-sighted to present so much repetition that the excitement of discovery and hypothesizing is lost.

## Number bonds

Children need to have the 'addition facts' up to 10 (and preferably up to 20) at their finger tips by the time they are eight or so. There are so many good ideas for helping children learn these facts that it is difficult to see the argument for pages of sums. Of course, the children must practise adding-up, just as they must later practise subtraction. But there are many ways of doing this without resorting to 'mathematical colouring' where the teacher draws the outline (dictates the method to be used) and the child colours in the drawing (copies the algorithm). In order to help children develop their own methods and, as far as possible, set them in a meaningful context we need to consider alternatives.

### Building the bonds

Using Multilink or Unifix of two colours, children can build towers all the same height (Figure 1). They can then record the number bonds thus obtained. In this way all the possible bonds of any one number can be built, handled and demonstrated. It is important for some children to construct things which they need to remember, as well as to write or draw them, because the building process aids the memory.

### Curve stitching

This provides another method of illustrating number bonds. To show the bonds of 7, take a piece of card and mark the $x$ axis (horizontal) with the numbers from 0 to 7 and the $y$ axis (vertical) with the numbers from 7 to 0. Prick needle-holes along the axes beside each number. The child now takes a thread and stitches all the number bonds, joining the appropriate numbers 1 to 7, 2 to 6, etc. (Figure 2). The resulting curve shows these links clearly and

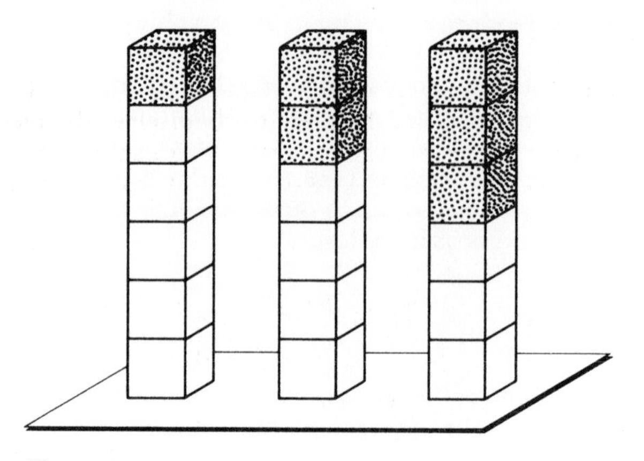

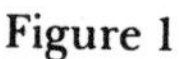

Figure 1

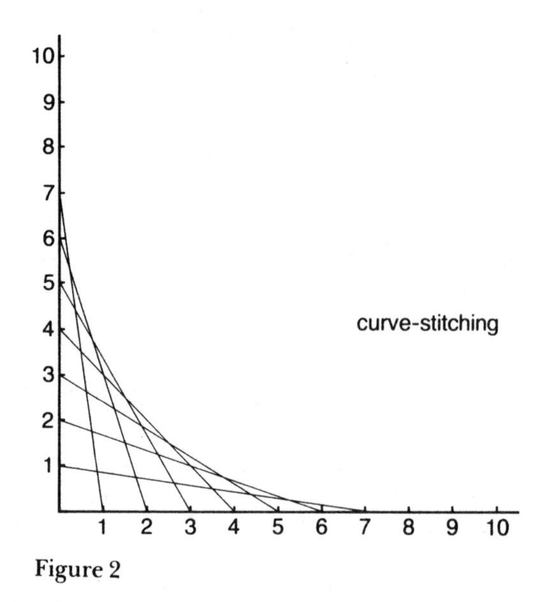


Figure 2

makes an attractive pattern.
Now the children can be encouraged to investigate:

1) bonds of other numbers in different coloured threads either on the same or on newly drawn axes;
2) the effect of varying the angle between the two axes.

These curves make a very attractive display, which encourages careful and precise work.

**Drawing number bonds**

Using a piece of squared paper it is possible to colour number bonds (Figure 3). The children can then see for themselves the fact that as one side decreases in steps so the opposite side increases. This fact, if really grasped by the children, helps them to work out unknown bonds.

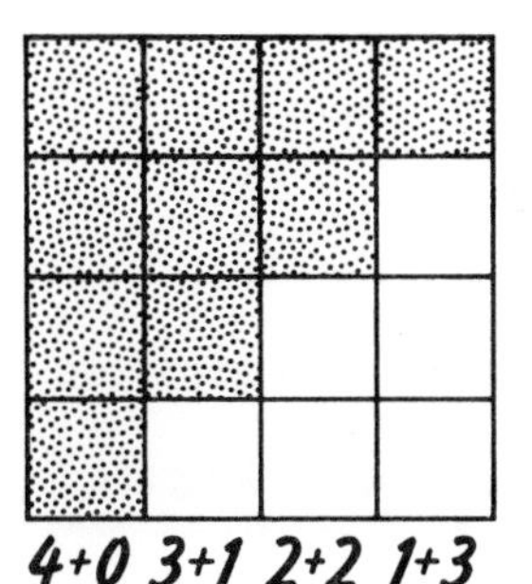


Figure 3

**Threading beads**

Children often enjoy threading two colours of beads on to a string. This can demonstrate the number of bonds very effectively. The number of each colour is counted and recorded.

**Dice activities**

A die or a pair of dice can be effectively used to reinforce number bonds and to motivate the children into doing a large number of 'sums' quickly and in their heads without really realizing that they are doing them.

Draw two axes on a piece of squared paper and number 1 to 12 consecutively along the bottom as shown (Figure 4). The 2 dice are thrown and their totals added. The square in the appropriate column is then coloured. The children have to throw the dice 50 times and mark the totals on the paper each time. But before they begin they must write down the number which they estimate will be most coloured. (Children generally guess at 12!) Having completed the graph the children then discuss why the most popular columns are always 6, 7 and 8: the children will have their own ideas about

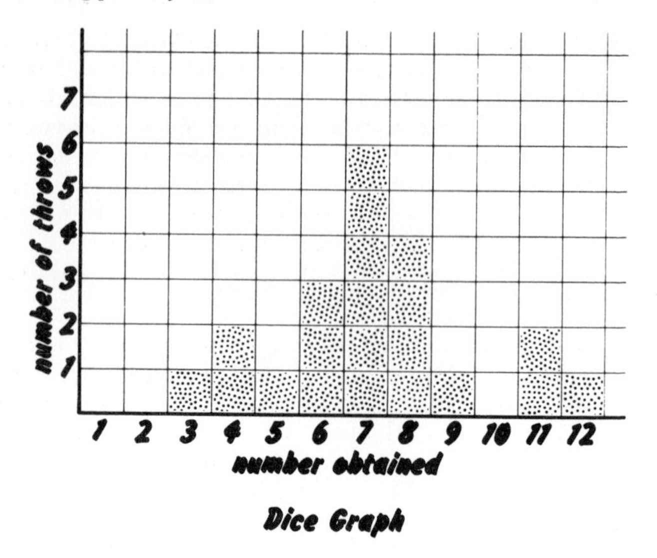


Figure 4

why these numbers come up so often.

A similar activity involves the children in shaking one die, doubling the number shown and colouring the appropriate square. The fact that no odd numbers get coloured will cause much comment and many of the children will be puzzled at first that this is so. This activity involves the children in doing over 50 sums in well under an hour. Once again, the completed sheets can be displayed to advantage with questions like: Why is 7 such a popular answer? A large die can be displayed to show that the opposite sides always add up to 7.

A short follow-up activity which children find almost magical is to stack 4 dice in a pile, then ask a child to say what the horizontal faces add up to. They immediately start to dismantle the pile in order to look and see what the numbers are on the faces. Very few children (or adults!) realize that, since the opposite faces on a die always add up to 7, there is no need to look at what these faces are – the answer must be 7 + 7 + 7 + 7, or 28.

## Dominoes

(*i*) Dominoes, like dice or cards, are a very useful resource when it comes to getting children to practise addition. Children can be encouraged to lay dominoes in a line in such a way that the touching ends always add up to 6. If a domino track is drawn out and mounted on card with a suitable pair of objects, such as a king and his crown, a dog and its bone or a rocket and a planet, pictured at either end of the track, it makes a very attractive board game which, covered in clear adhesive film, will last for a long time. It is a useful resource for a teacher to have three or four of these boards for the children to take out and play with as they want to. An alternative for smaller children is for them to lay the dominoes end to end by matching numbers as in the traditional game of dominoes. Even so it is not as easy as might at first be imagined to get all the way round the track from the dog to its bone.

(*ii*) Worksheets using dominoes can be produced by asking the children to draw all the dominoes in the box which have 7 dots on them. The child has then to perform a number of addition sums in order to ascertain which dominoes must be drawn. They will add up a number of dominoes which do not add up to 7 (e.g. 5 and 3), as well as those that do. Variations on this theme involve changing the number of dots, asking them to look for all the dominoes which have 8 dots or 6 dots (very difficult). Alternatively, the children can be asked to draw those dominoes with more than 6 dots or less than 6 dots.

## Cards

The use of cards to play games which help reinforce the number bonds can be very helpful. Some common and useful card games include:

(*i*) Pelmanism. In this game a pack of 44 cards numbered from 0 to 10 four times are used. Lay the cards out on the floor or a table face-down. The children then take turns to turn up a pair of cards. If the cards turned up add up to 10 then the child may take them and keep them. If not, they are turned face-down and the next person has a go. The winner is the child who has collected the most pairs when all the cards are gone.

The game provides a good incentive for children to remember their bonds to 10 and develops their memories.

(*ii*) Snap. This game is played as in the usual version but 'snap' may only be called if the 2 exposed cards add up to 10.

(*iii*) Fish. In this game 5 cards are dealt to each player and the remainder placed in a pile face-down in the middle. The children take it in turns to ask another person if s/he has a number which will add to one they already hold to make a 10. Thus, if a child has a 3, they may ask: 'Have you got a 7, Tom?' If Tom has a 7, he must hand it over. If he has no 7 he replies 'Fish' and the asker must 'fish' a card off the central pile and add it to their hand. The player with the most pairs wins.

### Board games

Once again, there are many different appropriate board games, which reinforce number bonds and practise addition:

(*i*) Snakes and ladders. The children are asked to make their own snakes and ladders game. The younger children can use a grid 6 squares by 6 squares, and the older children 8 by 8 or 10 by 10. These grids can then be mounted on brightly-coloured card, the squares numbered and the snakes and ladders (a limited number of each – say 3) put in where the child wants them. Having made their board and decorated it, the children play the game, perhaps employing variations such as throwing 2 dice and adding the totals. The idea of addition as counting on is reinforced by this game especially with young children. The display of the boards can be very effective and can encourage a number of questions as to the best place to put the snakes!

(*ii*) Castle game. A picture of a castle is drawn on 2 separate boards. The windows are then marked with numbers which represent some possible sums of 2 dice scores (Figure 5). Each child then takes it in turns to shake the dice, add the totals and cover the appropriate window with a toy soldier. When every window is covered, the castle is deemed to be guarded and the game ends. Different pictures such as rockets with numbered planets to visit, or bunches of flowers with numbered centres can also be used. Choose a picture which you think will most appeal to the children in the group. 3 or 4 pairs of boards, all different, are a handy resource in the classroom.

## Early place value

From middle infants onwards, it is important that children start developing those ideas of grouping and exchange which form the basis of a sound understanding of place value. Failure to grasp the concept of place value is the most frequent cause of computational difficulties later on. If children have not understood that in 22 the first 2 has a different value from the second because of its place they will be unable to perform the necessary algorithms in junior school and beyond.

It has already been suggested that children learning to count

Figure 5

should 'group' things in order to count efficiently (chapter 3, p.17). The children will also be familiar with the idea of a set. So some children will be ready from the middle infants onwards to start playing grouping and exchange games.

## Grouping activities

There are many sets of objects within the day-to-day experience of the child which can be put in to groups in the sense we want for this purpose. For example, they can group eggs (preferably hard-boiled or painted ones) into boxes, so that if they have 14 eggs, these may be grouped into 2 boxes and there will be 2 spare eggs. Cakes may be grouped into cake tins, chocolate bars into packets, etc. It is important that the children handle and group the objects themselves. A worksheet to go alongside these activities can be a good means of recording.

## Games

There are many good games in this area. The basic idea is always that the children are encouraged to exchange a certain number of things in the right-hand column for one thing in the left-hand column and so on.

(*i*) Beetle game. This game consists of collecting 6 legs for a beetle, and then 6 beetles for a family. The beetles can be made out of plasticine and the legs out of matchsticks or pipe-cleaners. The families can be collected in basket or box 'homes'. An ordinary die is thrown and the children collect legs to the value of the number thrown. When they have collected 6 legs they may exchange them for a beetle, etc. The first person to collect a family is the winner.

(*ii*) Cat game. This is played exactly as the above game but this time the children collect legs to exchange for cats, and cats for houses or flats. The game is played 4 legs to a cat, and 4 cats to a house or flat. This is a speedier game than the beetle one because the base is lower. There are many other games along this line.

The educational objectives of these games are to develop the concepts of grouping and exchange and so it is never necessary to convert from one base to another at this level.

## Tallying activities

The children can be encouraged to record by tallying in groups of 5. The usual method of recording is given in Figure 6. The child takes a handful of dried beans and then counts and groups them. It is not necessary for the children to record the number of beans in base 10.

Figure 6

## Justification for early multi-base work

It used to be felt that multi-base work was appropriate only further up the junior school, once the children had become familiar with base 10. But the point of working in bases under 10 is not that we need to do so for its own sake. It is rather that we need children to develop the concepts of grouping, exchange and, ultimately, place value. Using base 10 materials for this purpose with young children is counter-productive because of the sheer number of objects that they have to deal with. In order to get into three columns in base 10 they must count and handle over 100 objects. This means that the children get 'lost' in the counting required and the concept of place value is harder to acquire. So it proves much easier to begin by grouping in bases below 10 where we have to deal with fewer objects. Working in base 3 the children only need 9 objects to be in three columns, in base 4 (like the 'cat' game), they need 16. Under these circumstances they are much more likely to acquire the concepts of exchange and place value.

**Place value game**

*Playing the place value game using children as 'counters' in different columns*

This game makes a very good intermediate stage between the grouping activities mentioned earlier and structural base apparatus. It can be made by the children and can be played in groups or as a class game. It is immensely versatile and also good fun.

Each child first makes their own board which consists of a piece of A4 paper folded lengthways in half and in half again. Each of the four columns thus obtained are now coloured. All the children playing in one particular group must have the same coloured boards. A pile of Multilink in those colours and a die are now placed in the middle of each group. Each child now throws the die in turn and takes the shown number of counters of the colour of the right-hand column on their paper and places them on that column (Figure 7). When they have 3 or more counters in that column, those 3 may be exchanged for one of the next colour along. In this way the child will gradually acquire counters of colours further along the board. The first person to get a counter of the colour of the left-hand column is the winner. A player throwing a 1 has another turn! This game is very fast and the children get quite proficient at the grouping and exchanging skills involved. Questions such as: 'How many must you throw now to catch up, Julie?' and 'Who is winning now?' put to the children as they play will require some careful thought on their part.

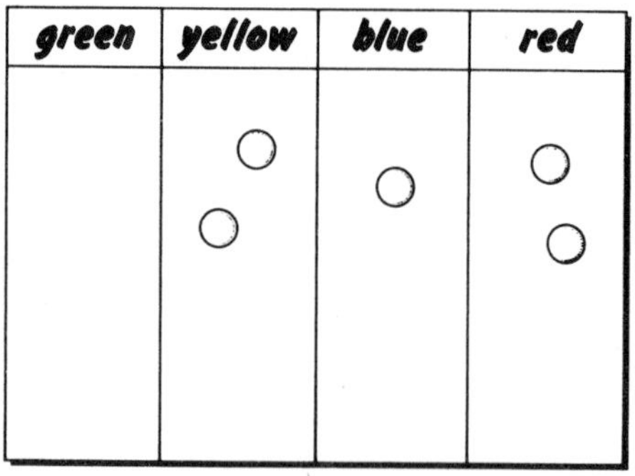

| green | yellow | blue | red |
|---|---|---|---|
| | | | |

3 red = 1 blue

3 blue = 1 yellow

3 yellow = 1 green

the number on the dice = the number of reds to be taken

Figure 7

The game can be turned into a class activity. Each child sits with a board and a heap of Multilink, or the children can work in pairs. The teacher needs a bell and a wooden clapper. When the bell is rung, the children must put one Multilink into the right-hand column. When they collect three in this column, they must exchange them as before. When the clapper is sounded, the children must remove one Multilink from the right-hand column. It is very interesting to watch what happens when the clapper is sounded and the children only have one Multilink in the next column along from the right. This is really decomposition in action! This game can easily be made into a 'team' game if required.

**Structural base apparatus**

Once children are quite familiar with the fact that they are able to move from one column to another by grouping and exchanging, they are ready to work in base 10 with structural apparatus. They begin with a base board (Figure 8) with either 'hundreds', 'tens', and 'units' or 'squares', 'longs' and 'ones' written on it. They then perform the same sort of grouping and exchange activities that they have been performing with the lower-base games and activities. They may take a large handful of small beads and count them using the base 10 apparatus to record their figures, laying out the 'tens' rods and the unit blocks as they count. The advantage of the base apparatus here is that a rod is a different object from a unit block and an exchange of 10 for 1 must be made. The same obviously applies to squares.

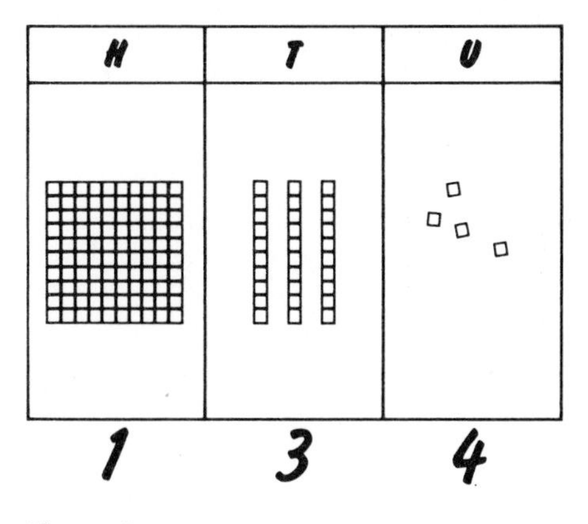


Figure 8

An abacus demonstrates much the same thing as base 10 structural apparatus but in a much more abstract way. It is more useful later on, when used either to help with computations, or to assist with the introduction of decimal work.

Two children can work together with advantage on the base 10 apparatus. They take a large handful of beads each and count them on to their respective boards. They then amalgamate the two boards and perform the necessary regroupings to calculate the addition.

## Arithmetical objectives in the infant school

In the infant school there are clear educational objectives when doing number work:

### Numbers and counting

Children should come to a clear understanding of the different functions numbers serve and of efficient ways of establishing number by counting.

### Conservation of number

Children must develop the concept of conservation of number. They should understand the 'fiveness' of 5.

### Addition and subtraction

Children should have clear ideas of addition and subtraction. This can include counting on, combining sets, taking away from, and finding the difference between.

### Place value

This concept must be clearly understood if the children are to progress satisfactorily from now on. It will involve the ideas of grouping and exchange.

### Estimation

The children can practise estimating from a very young age. They can often 'guess' how many, or try to put an accurate number to a row of beads or a Multilink model.

### Sense of number

A 'feel' for numbers is important and children should have played with number patterns and some of the various properties of number: odd/even; prime; square; triangular, etc.

## Relations between the different operations

The relationship between addition, subtraction, multiplication and division is easily expressed in a diagram (Figure 9).

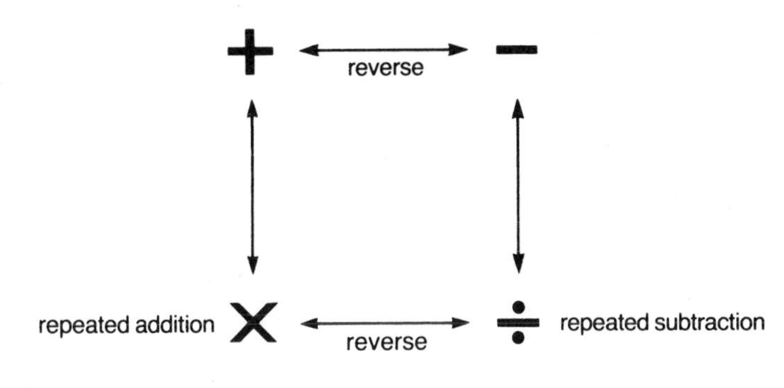


Figure 9

### Individual operations

(*i*) Addition. This is a relatively simple concept to develop. It matches the use of the word 'and' in language. It can be demonstrated using a variety of objects.

(*ii*) Subtraction. This is a more complex operation which can involve the notion of 'difference', as in 'the difference between 7 and 13 is 6'. It can also involve the idea of 'taking-away'.

(*iii*) Multiplication. This is repeated addition. It can be seen as taking a number of steps, all the same size, along the number line.

(*iv*) Division. Like subtraction, this is a complex operation. It can involve sharing out a certain number of objects amongst a defined number of people. Alternatively, it can be shown by repeatedly subtracting the same number from a pre-determined figure.

## Early calculator activities

There is a definite place for the calculator in the infant school. Both the Cockcroft Report and the more recent HMI document have recommended the use of calculators in school.

Calculators can be used in three ways:

### As a teaching aid

They can be used – in much the same way that any structural apparatus such as Multilink is used – to help the children develop a particular concept. Some useful activities in this connection include:

(*i*) Children 'put' a big number on the display. They can show as big a number as they like, with the proviso that they must be able to say what the number is. This produces some very interesting language and gives a very useful insight into the stage the children's learning has reached.

(*ii*) Children use the calculator to add 10 repeatedly to a specific number (e.g. 6 + 10 = 16 + 10 = 26 + 10 = 36 etc.). They are able to see the pattern thus obtained immediately since they are not confused by having to concentrate on a lot of sums. We do not want children to have to calculate 25 + 10, we want them to know the answer because of their understanding of place value and their knowledge of the number pattern obtained when 10 is added.

(*iii*) The children are asked to remove the 3 from 32 without removing the 2. They are allowed to press any keys except 'cancel' or 'cancel entry'. This is a place value activity and is a very helpful diagnostic test.

### As a help in difficult calculations

Sometimes the children are involved in some activity which requires them to do a calculation which at this point they do not have the necessary skills to perform. For example, they might have counted vehicles passing the school in a type of traffic survey. This might lead to the need to add 45 + 56 + 13 + 27 + 9. A calculator is highly suitable in this situation since the children simply need a quick and not frustrating means to an end. Of course they have to understand the operations entailed in order to know what buttons to push. Once again, this can make a useful diagnostic test.

### As a means of teaching 'calculator skills'

It is clear from the evidence that many people now have access to a calculator at home and that they use one at work. However, calculators are mostly used very inefficiently. People do not know which buttons to push or what the memory does, etc. It is important that, from very early on, children pick up the habit of using the calculator as efficiently as possible. To do this, they must be given time to 'play' with the machine, write names on it (0.7734 = HELLO), and explore what the various keys do. Even small children can use the constant facility whereby the calculator goes on doing what it was told to do last. They can also be encouraged to make the calculator 'remember' their age. This is very popular with middle infants or reception children.

At this age children need to familiarize themselves with the keyboard. Drawing the calculator is a good means of doing this. Early number work benefits greatly from the use of the calculator. It is bound to be a part of the mathematics curriculum for the 1990s.

# 5

# Subtraction, multiplication and division

## Subtraction

Subtraction is one of the concepts which children acquire very early on. If we put 6 sweets on Fred's plate and 3 sweets on Julie's plate, Julie will cry even though she is too young to object verbally. This fact, well known to parents, is an indication of how early children acquire the concept of 'difference'. The idea that one amount differs from another and by a certain amount, is one part of subtraction. The other is the idea of 'taking away' or decomposition. This can be shown by taking a handful of counters, counting them and taking some away.

## Methods of demonstrating or calculating the difference between two amounts

### Cuisenaire Rods or Colour Factor

Cuisenaire or Colour Factor rods are very useful in this connection. The children should be given some time at first to simply play with the rods in order to get familiar with the materials, but they will quickly recognize the number represented by each rod. Often the numbers do not even have to be pointed out by the teacher since the children will label the rods of their own accord. Two rods of different sizes can be put together. The difference between the two numbers is made up by counting out unit blocks. Alternatively, a rod is found which exactly fills the gap and the number it represents is noted (Figure 1). This provides a very practical and memorable way of showing the difference between two numbers. The children's experiences can be recorded by drawing out rod-shaped strips on squared paper and colouring the differences.

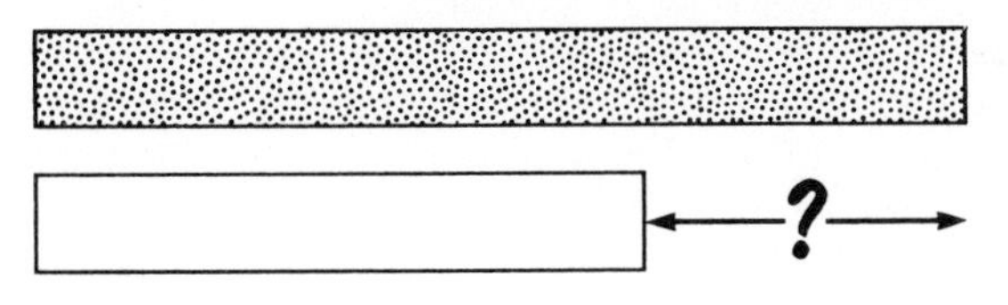


Figure 1

**Sets of counters or Multilink**

Make sets of two different colours of Multilink by putting a handful of, say, red on one plate and a handful of, say, blue on another. First an estimation of which plate has more is made. Then the Multilink is matched one-to-one, a red one from one plate to a blue one from the other, and clipped together in pairs. When one plate is empty, the number left over is the difference – or the answer to the subtraction sum. This mapping of one set on to another in a one-to-one correspondence follows on from their earlier work on sets (chapter 2).

**Using the number line and counting on**

The number line, familiar by now, makes an excellent way of computing the difference in a more formal way. Once the difference between two numbers has been demonstrated using Cuisenaire Rods, it can then be worked out using the number line in much the same way as it was used for calculating addition sums. This method of calculating subtraction sums has the added advantage that it leads to 'gazuptas' or what is called 'shopkeepers' addition' later on. The child has a number line and counts *on* from the smaller number to the larger number (Figure 2).

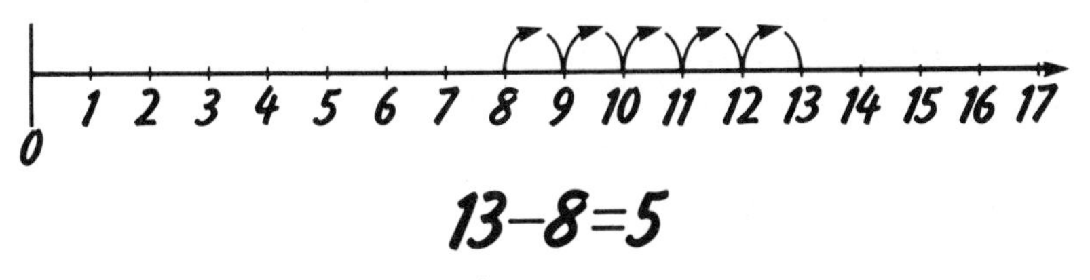


Figure 2

This mirrors exactly what happens when one Cuisenaire rod is placed up against another and unit cubes are used to make up the difference. The same physical representation can be achieved through building two towers of different heights and then counting how many blocks have to be added to the smaller tower to make it the same height as the other. The number line is the formal representation of this and can prove a helpful means to the efficient and fast computation of subtraction.

### Subtraction as it arises out of the context of measures

The children will meet the concept of difference as it arises out of the context of other work. An obvious case is that of measuring, especially in length, where the child will often see that there is a difference in height or length and will express this difference in terms of some numbers. Thus, one handspan may prove to be 18 cm long, and another 15 cm long. The child may be required to give the difference as 3 cm.

Under these circumstances where the 'difference' or comparative aspect of subtraction is not forgotten amidst too great an accent on 'taking-away' sums children are able to make the connections across the curriculum which will enable them to use the computations that they learn in maths outside the classroom as well as in it. Comparisons often involve subtraction – the train takes 2 hours to get to Bristol, the car takes 3 hours, how much longer is the journey by car? Or, weighing flour for a cake and finding that there are 200 grams left in the bag, and that the recipe calls for 350 grams, how much more do I need? Subtraction sums – in the sense of finding the difference – arise out of all sorts of contexts and, as the HMI document, Curriculum Matters No. 3 says: 'At various points in this document comments are made about the undesirability of over-emphasizing the practising and testing of certain skills out of context.' It goes on to recommend that, where possible, computational skills should be developed in appropriate contexts.

### Money sums and 'gazuptas'

When a transaction is taking place in a shop or market, the means of calculating change is what is called 'shopkeepers' addition' or 'gazupta'. The person giving the change and performing the subtraction counts on up from the figure owed to the figure given. Thus, if I owe the milkman £2.37 and I pay with a £5 note, he works out my change by counting up: £2.37 + 3p makes £2.40, + 10p makes £2.50 and 50p makes £3; finally £2 more makes the fiver. This method can be used successfully in class. First play at giving change and counting on up, using small amounts of money only. Start with 20p. The 'shopper' wants something for 7p and offers a 20p coin to pay for it. Giving the change will involve counting up from 7 to 20. As the calculations get more complex, they can be written thus (Figure 3). This method of subtracting can be extended to more and more difficult subtractions, if required.

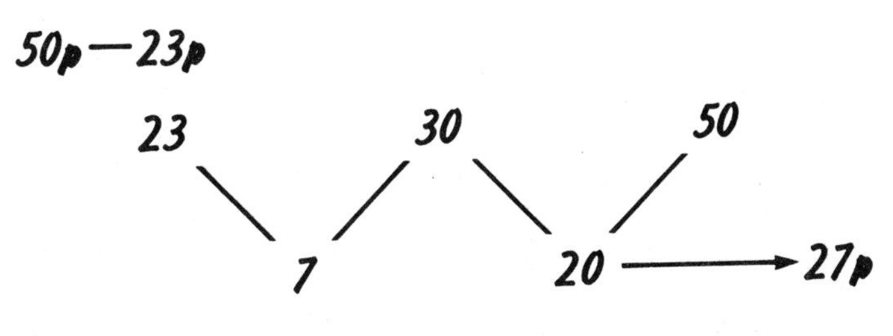


Figure 3

## Decomposition and 'taking away'

### Using counters or Multilink

The children can do 'taking away' sums in pairs using counters or bricks. A handful of either is taken and counted. The number is recorded. Some counters (or bricks) are then removed and counted. This number is also written down. Finally the number remaining are counted and recorded. This is a very cumbersome way of performing a subtraction sum, but it does have the advantage that what is happening is very obvious. Most children will not need to do very many sums like this or they will quickly become bored. It is more fun if the sums are done in pairs and it also makes more sense, mathematically speaking!

### Using a number line

Subtraction can be seen as the reverse of addition and can be performed by counting back along the number line as opposed to counting forwards in addition. The advantage of this is that it is much quicker and less cumbersome than the method outlined above which is really only suitable for demonstrating what decomposition is about. The number line provides a speedy and efficient means of working out the answer to a subtraction sum. For example, 13 − 8 can be performed by counting backwards from 13 to 8 and seeing how many steps were taken. This method has the advantage over the former that only one thing has to be counted (i.e. the steps between two numbers, rather than three sets of objects). This reduces the possibility of error from three to one, since children frequently make mistakes in counting, especially when it becomes boring.

## Decomposition using a base board

Later on, some children will learn to subtract on a board such as the one suggested on page 40 for use in place value activities. This method of subtraction is now standardly taught using decomposition, that is to say by breaking down the figure in the next column when necessary (tens into units, hundreds into tens, etc.). This method is preferred precisely because it can be demonstrated using place value apparatus, such as Dienes or Tillichs blocks (Figure 4).

There is some dispute now about the relevance of this sort of paper and pencil calculation to the everyday needs of children or adults today. Most people have access to a calculator and use one when necessary at work. This fact means that it is important to look hard at what is taught and how, to ensure that it is applicable to the world in which we live. As the HMI document states: 'If mathematics is only about computational skills out of context, it cannot be justified as a subject in the curriculum.' It is necessary that the type of written method of doing subtraction sums described above no longer occupies the central position in the number curriculum.'

## Using a calculator

Whenever possible, children can be encouraged to estimate their answer before calculating it accurately. This will help them to develop a sense of the approximate 'size' of the expected answer as well as making them think about the subtraction itself. Sometimes children will use a calculator to help them develop a sense of when to do a subtraction sum without worrying too much about the actual mechanics of doing it. So if a child measures the length of a room in order to find the length of wall available for a display and then realizes that s/he has forgotten to allow for the window space, it may be much more important to know that s/he understands that a subtraction sum is required and that the answer is *about* 5 metres, than to spend a great deal of time and energy actually doing the sum

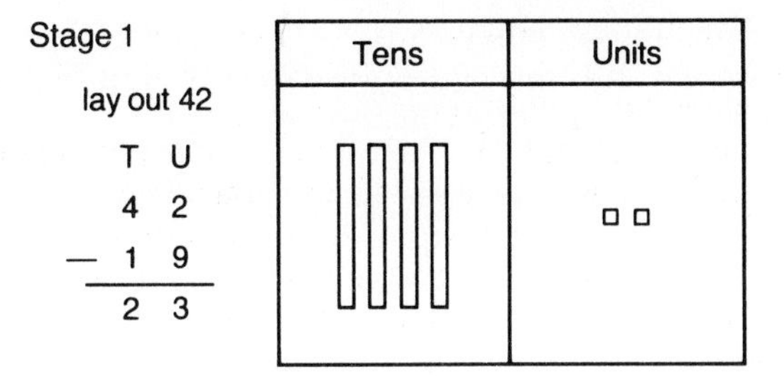


Stage 2

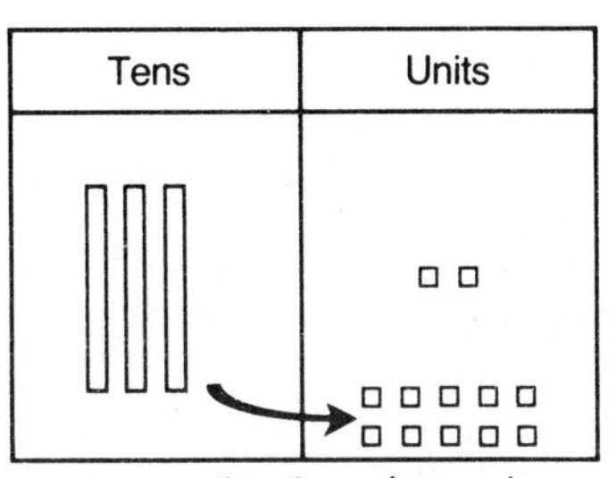


remove one 'long', exchange it
for 10 units and 'take away' 9

Stage 3

Tens | Units

take away one 'ten'

Figure 4

with paper and pencil, especially if practising that particular skill is not the point of that exercise. The calculator can be invaluable both in terms of games and activities and also in terms of a useful classroom resource. Helpful activities include:

(*i*) Extending the place value game mentioned on pages 39–40. The child puts a three-figure number on the screen, for example, 534, and must now attempt to 'knock down' the middle digit and then the left-hand digit and finally the last digit. A digit is deemed to have been knocked down when a nought appears in its place. The child may press any keys they want except 'C' or 'CE'. It is often some while before the children realize, usually through trial and error, that they have first to subtract 30 and not 3!

(*ii*) Some of the general calculator activities can help to give a child a greater fluency with subtraction. If the number of keys which may be used is restricted to 3, 7, –, × and =, then the child can be asked to obtain all the numbers from 1 to 20 on the screen. This will involve a large number of subtraction sums as well as considerable ingenuity. It may well turn into a mini-investigation – which two numbers, coupled with which two operations will 'work'? Which ones will not?

## Introducing multiplication

Multiplication is first seen as groups or sets of objects.

Count out Multilink, clip it into groups of 3 and shade on a 0 – 99 number square each time a group is completed. This gives the pattern of the 3 times table. The same activity can be repeated using groups of 2 or groups of 4, etc.

The objective here is twofold:-

1) To demonstrate that multiplication involves numbers of identical sets. Thus 4 × 3 means 4 sets of 3 and is often written 4(3) to emphasize this at the same time facilitating the progression to algebraic forms such as $4(x)$ or $4(3 + x)$.
2) To develop a sense of pattern and in particular of the number patterns involved in multiplication. This:
   – assists in the memorizing of tables;
   – leads on to a study of series and progressions, such as arithmetic and geometric progressions, in the secondary school;
   – develops a feeling of ease with numbers, an awareness of their properties (even/odd, divides by 3, square, etc.) and a sense of how they behave.

The introduction of multiplication should include:

a) plenty of practice at grouping objects into sets and counting how many there are (e.g. 2 chairs have 8 legs, 3 chairs have 12 legs, 4 chairs have 16 legs, etc.). This is essential if the children are to understand what multiplication is in order to use it in contexts other than tables tests!

b) plenty of experiences involving number squares (0–99), tables squares and tables patterns. The following are some suggestions.

(*i*) Make a 0–99 square on 2 cm squared paper. Use it in conjunction with Multilink. Place a pink block on every even number, a blue block on every third number and a red one on every fourth number. In this way a 3-d model of factors and products can be built up. This activity can be recorded by colouring a series of number squares.

(*ii*) A factor investigation suitable for second-year juniors involves asking the children to draw as many different rectangles as possible which cover a specified number of squares (e.g. 24). They draw a 2 by 12 oblong, a 3 by 8, a 4 by 6 and maybe a 1 by 24 if the paper is long enough. By varying the specified number and including some square numbers, and even some primes, the children can discover quite a lot about factors and how they work. This activity provides enough work for several sessions over a week so that the children have time to think and reflect on the problem. The resulting rectangles, when coloured, make a lovely display. A calculator can be used to assist in the trial and error process of finding factors. How to use a calculator to do this is itself a problem for some children.

(*iii*) Digital roots. This activity assists in the memorizing of tables but is also a fascinating illustration of the significance of the number 9 in our base 10 number system. Write down a multiplication table e.g. the 4 times table) and add the digits of each number. (If the sum of the digits is a double figure, add the 2 digits together.) The single number obtained is the digital root.

| *4 times table:* | 4 | 8 | 12 | 16 | 20 | 24 | 28 | 32 | 36 | 40 | 44 | 48 | 52 |
|---|---|---|---|---|---|---|---|---|---|---|---|---|---|
| *digital root:* | 4 | 8 | 3 | 7 | 2 | 6 | 10 | 5 | 9 | 4 | 8 | 12 | 7 |
| | | | | | | | 1 | | | | | 3 | |

The repeated series is drawn out on squared paper by drawing lines of the unit lengths given by the series of digital roots and turning 90° clockwise at the end of each line (Figure 5). This produces a spiral.

Different children can try this using different tables. Do they all give a repeating series? Are any of the spirals (or series) the same? If so, which ones? Predict what spiral the 13 times table will produce.

This activity is immense fun for the children, they almost all enjoy it and it can produce a really spectacular display. In some cases, some quite advanced mathematics is performed.

(*iv*) Properties of multiplication, for example, commutativity, can be demonstrated neatly using a tables square, (Figure 6). Colour the even numbers on a tables square and it will be seen that there are more even numbers than odd on the square by 3:1. This is because:

– an even number multiplied by an even number gives an even number;

– an even number multiplied by an odd number gives an even number.

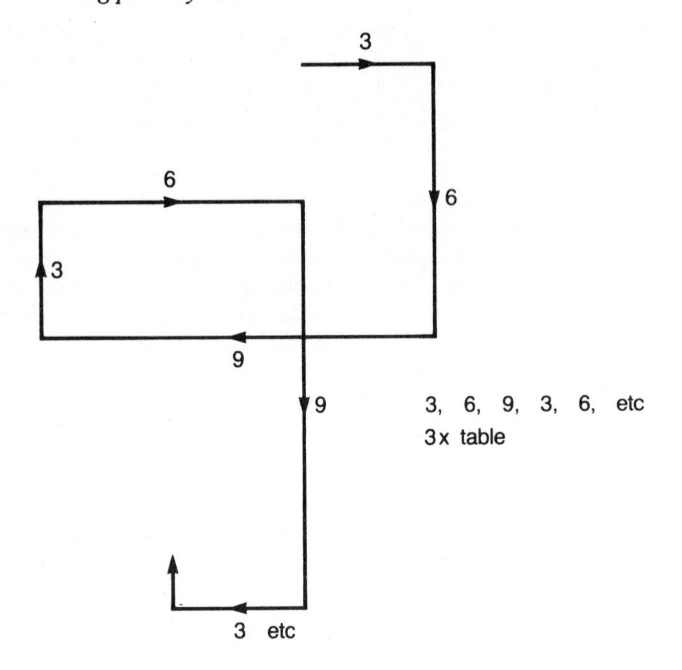


Figure 5

| 1 | 2 | 3 | 4 | 5 | 6 | 7 | 8 | 9 | 10 |
|---|---|---|---|---|---|---|---|---|---|
| 2 | 4 | 6 | 8 | 10 | 12 | 14 | 16 | 18 | 20 |
| 3 | 6 | 9 | 12 | 15 | 18 | 21 | 24 | 27 | 30 |
| 4 | 8 | 12 | 16 | 20 | 24 | 28 | 32 | 36 | 40 |
| 5 | 10 | 15 | 20 | 25 | 30 | 35 | 40 | 45 | 50 |
| 6 | 12 | 18 | 24 | 30 | 36 | 42 | 48 | 54 | 60 |
| 7 | 14 | 21 | 28 | 35 | 42 | 49 | 56 | 63 | 70 |
| 8 | 16 | 24 | 32 | 40 | 48 | 56 | 64 | 72 | 80 |
| 9 | 18 | 27 | 36 | 45 | 54 | 63 | 72 | 81 | 90 |
| 10 | 20 | 30 | 40 | 50 | 60 | 70 | 80 | 90 | 100 |

**line of symmetry**

Figure 6

It can also be seen that the tables square is symmetrical about its leading diagonal. If a tables square is folded along this diagonal, dropped and caught again between finger and thumb, the squares where the finger and thumb touch are likely to be the same. This is because multiplication is commutative, that is to say: 3 × 4 is the same as 4 × 3.

Thus when children are learning the tables square they only need to learn half of it. This is important to note otherwise we double the number of facts. If they learn the 2 times table and the 7 times table as separate entities they are learning one fact twice, that 2 × 7 = 14 and 7 × 2 = 14. They do not necessarily relate the two facts and this is an important omission.

c) memorizing the tables 'facts'. The tables square (Figure 7) can form the basis for the number facts to be learned by children and the more these facts are on instant recall the better. It must be remembered that number facts usually only remain on tap in this way if they are being constantly used so it should come as no surprise if the children who seemed to be 'tables perfect' before the summer holidays appear to have forgotten them all by September. However, if the tables facts have been understood, are set within a context and form part of a larger system of number patterns, instant recall will be easily regained in a short time.

| 1 | 2 | 3 | 4 | 5 | 6 | 7 | 8 | 9 | 10 |
|---|---|---|---|---|---|---|---|---|---|
| 2 | 4 | 6 | 8 | 10 | 12 | 14 | 16 | 18 | 20 |
| 3 | 6 | 9 | 12 | 15 | 18 | 21 | 24 | 27 | 30 |
| 4 | 8 | 12 | 16 | 20 | 24 | 28 | 32 | 36 | 40 |
| 5 | 10 | 15 | 20 | 25 | 30 | 35 | 40 | 45 | 50 |
| 6 | 12 | 18 | 24 | 30 | 36 | 42 | 48 | 54 | 60 |
| 7 | 14 | 21 | 28 | 35 | 42 | 49 | 56 | 63 | 70 |
| 8 | 16 | 24 | 32 | 40 | 48 | 56 | 64 | 72 | 80 |
| 9 | 18 | 27 | 36 | 45 | 54 | 63 | 72 | 81 | 90 |
| 10 | 20 | 30 | 40 | 50 | 60 | 70 | 80 | 90 | 100 |

Figure 7

To assist the memorizing of these number facts it helps to divide up the square. A suggested ordering of learning tables is as follows:

– concentrating on the vertical columns starting from the left, the first column is the counting numbers so no learning is required here;

– the second column is the doubles and these also should already be known;

– the third column is the sum of the first two columns and does not normally prove difficult to learn.

It is useful to look next at the bottom line or row which is the 10 times table and usually requires little or no memorizing at this stage. The 9 times table, or penultimate column (or row), is best learnt using the finger method shown later or noting the facts that the two numbers of the product always add up to 9 and the first number is one less than the number multiplied by 9, for example, $4 \times 9 = 36$ $(3 + 6 = 9)$.

The 5 times table, the fifth column or row, is also easy to learn especially if chanted.

The square numbers which form the leading diagonal should be easily learnt if sufficient work on squares, triangular numbers, the sums of difference of squares (chapter 6) has already been done.

The fourth column is double the second and can always be obtained by doubling up though this one does not usually prove difficult to learn.

The hard-to-learn tables facts are those in the 6, 7, and 8 times tables that have not already been acquired. These products are 42, 48, 56, 72 and they are most commonly mis-remembered or forgotten. But when the difficulty is pinned down to just four number facts many children find it less daunting than feeling insecure about the whole of the 6, 7 and 8 times tables. Therefore they will frequently make the necessary effort to commit these facts to memory.

This then is the advantage of recognizing the commutativity of multiplication: a child need only learn half the number of facts they would have to learn by memorizing each table separately.

## Different methods of improving the recall of tables

### Memorizing by chanting the tables

There is obviously a place for chanting the tables as one means among many to aid the memory. But it must be remembered that it is as important that the children learn that $3 \times 4 = 4 \times 3$ and that $3 \times 4$ is an even number because any number multiplied by an even number is even, as it is that they learn that three fours are twelve.

### Bingo games

These games are very useful indeed in helping children achieve instant recall on their tables. Boards can be made using 0–99 number squares. The children each have a board. Each child then throws two 10 sided dice or selects 2 cards from a pack from which the face cards have been removed. The 2 numbers are then multiplied and the product covered on the square. The first person to obtain 3 covered squares in a row in any direction, wins. If a longer game is required it can be 4 squares in a row and so on.

### Drawing tables graphs

Graphs of the multiplication tables can be drawn on squared paper by numbering the $x$ axis from 1–10 and the $y$ axis from 1–100. The co-ordinates of each table are then plotted and joined up, each in a different colour. The resulting graphical representations not only act as a memory enhancer, they also connect with algebra and the graphing of functions when children are required to do exactly the same thing in secondary school, drawing $y=2x$, $y=3x$ etc. on graphs.

### Curve stitching

Just as this was useful as a means of learning number bonds in the infant school (chapter 3), so it can be used as a means of learning tables. The axes are numbered as before and the appropriate numbers are joined by stitching up through the $x$ axis and down through the $y$ axis (Figure 8). More than one table can be stitched on one pair of axes using button thread or cotton.

### Practical work and multiplication in context

The more the tables are practised as problems involving products arising out of another context, the more likely it is the children will not only commit these facts to memory but retain them. If children learn a series of number facts simply for a test or in order to please a teacher at a certain time, these facts are less likely to be retained once the necessity is passed. So if we want the tables to be learnt and to stay learnt, it is exceedingly important that the necessity for using multi-

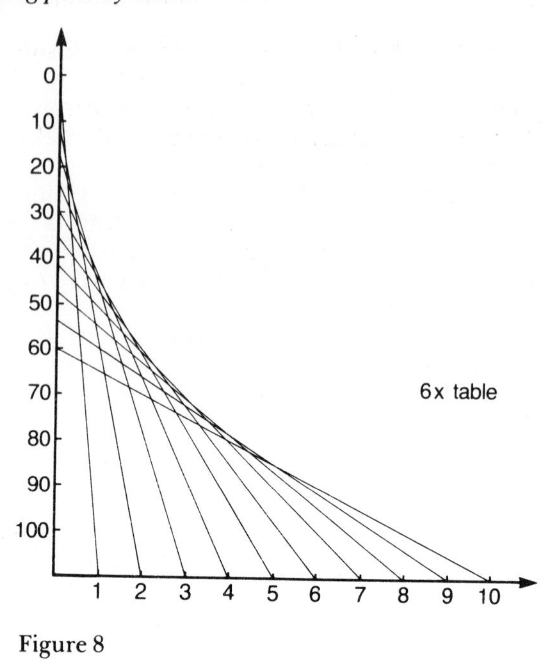


Figure 8

plication tables arises in contexts other than a tables test. It is not difficult to arrange this. Multiplication can arise out of area work or money calculations. Once children are aware that they can short-cut the process of repeated addition (e.g. by multiplying 4 × 7 instead of adding up 7 four times), they will naturally use multiplication and require their tables.

While children are learning their tables it does no harm for them to have their multiplication squares to hand to consult if necessary. It is quicker and easier than working the answer out although it should be possible for the child to do that as well. If they can sometimes obtain an answer instantly without too much hassle they are more inclined to memorize it.

## Calculator usage

A calculator can actively assist in the process of memorizing number facts. For example, children using the constant facility can make the calculator 'say' its 7 times table. All the products in the 7 times table must appear on the screen in the right order: 7, 14, 21, 28, 35, 42, 49 . . . To make the calculator do this it is necessary to press 7 + 7 = = and not 7 × 7 = =. Most children (and adults!) try using the × sign before they remember that multiplication is repeated addition.

The calculator can also patiently and uncritically give the answer to a table question again and again. Thus a child can rehearse a particular table they are finding hard. They can also take the tables further than the 10 times table if they want. This is especially useful when doing an investigation such as the one on digital roots.

Calculators can also be used by pairs of children to play games which require them to multiply to give a correct answer. The calculator is an easy means of checking an answer given by an opponent.

## Verbal games

Games such as 'the number in the pocket' or 'guess the rule' make excellent fill-ins for a ten-minute period as they are class games requiring few or no resources.

(*i*) The number in the pocket. The teacher announces that she has a number in her pocket and asks the children to guess it. They may ask any indirect questions they choose to establish its identity. Examples of indirect questions are: Is it prime? Does it divide by 3? Is it less than 50?

When the children think they know the answer they must find an indirect question suitable for checking it, for example, if they suspect that the number is 35 they can ask: Is it 7 × 5?

(*ii*) Guess the rule. In this game the teacher has a rule in mind which she applies to all numbers given to her. The children must guess this rule. They test the rule by calling out (one at a time!) a number and receiving and noting down the reply. Thus, if the child says 'five' and the teacher replies 'twenty-five', a possible hypothesis is that the rule is multiplying by 5. However if another child says 'four' and the reply is 'twenty-one' this theory is knocked on the head. The teacher must maintain the same rule as long as it takes the children to guess it. Once they have done so the game starts again. This game is quite hard and is best kept to the top half of the junior school.

(*iii*) Count round. The children count round the class in any specified number (e.g. in twos). Each child has a turn at saying a number in the series: 2, 4, 6 . . . This gives practice in counting in twos or threes, or whatever number is chosen, and helps to familiarize the children with the products in that particular table.

(*iv*) Fizzbuzz. This is a more complex version of count round in which the children count round in ones, but every time a number is reached which divides by 3 the child whose turn it is must not say that number but must say instead 'Fizz'. Similarly, every time a number is reached which divides by 5 the child must say 'Buzz' instead of the number. If a number is reached which has both 3 and 5 as factors, then the child must say 'Fizzbuzz'. So the counting starts: One, two, Fizz, four, Buzz, Fizz, seven, eight, Fizz, Buzz, eleven, Fizz, thirteen, fourteen, Fizzbuzz, etc. This game is quite difficult and takes a lot of practice to get it right. If a person says the wrong thing they must stand up and are deemed to be 'out'.

One final thing worth mentioning and which children enjoy very much is doing the tables on their fingers. When there was first a demand in Victorian times for large numbers of people who knew their tables because the factories all needed clerks to do their accounts and add up the figures in the order books, the schools taught tables on the fingers and that was the accepted method. Nowadays, we tend only to teach how to do the 9 times table on the fingers because it is the easiest and quickest to do using this method and because most children will have a stab at guessing why it works. The method is as follows: hold the hands out in front of you with fingers out-stretched. For example, if doing $5 \times 9$, turn down the fifth finger from the left. The answer is now shown by the fingers left standing. The fingers on the left of the turned down finger represent the tens and those on the right represent the units. Thus, in this case, the answer is 45.

## Division

Division, like subtraction, is really two concepts. It is sharing, that is, taking a specified number of objects and sharing them out evenly amongst a specified number of people: 15 shared among 3 is 5.

Division is also repeated subtraction: How many times can you take 4 away from 24?

Children do need lots of practice in sharing out objects and also in subtracting by hopping backwards along the number line.

Take a handful of objects and share them among 4 people. Count each handful and the remainder.

Arrays of squares of counters can be used to demonstrate division. To divide 24 by 6, take 24 Multilink and lay out 6 in a row, then 6 more underneath, then 6 more under those, etc. The number of rows gives the answer. This is a form of repeated subtraction – start with 24 and repeatedly deduct 6 – and it also demonstrates division as the reverse of multiplication. Just as when the children were learning multiplication they drew out factor rectangles (24 squares as 6 × 4 or 8 × 3) so in this case they divide by starting with the product and finding the second side of the rectangle if the first side is given. So 35 ÷ 7 can be layed out as one row of 7 after another until all 35 blocks are used up and there are 5 rows of blocks on the table. Once children see division not only as sharing but also as repeated subtraction or the opposite of multiplication, their tables will help them find the answer to many division sums without having to lay blocks or counters out.

It is important that remainders or left-overs form a part of division since in 'real life' things rarely share out equally. In this way children often come to see fractions as mini division sums. If 13 biscuits are being shared equally amongst 2 children they will have to have 6½ each.

Children should be aware of the horizontal line as a means of notating a division sum (Figure 9). This also makes explicit exactly what a fraction is: one third is 1 divided by 3.

There are many other ways of writing division sums (Figure 10) and children can sometimes become confused. Once again plenty of practical work is necessary to reinforce the idea of what is going on when one thing is divided by another.

$$\frac{36}{4} = 9$$

Figure 9

(i) $\frac{24}{6}$ (ii) $6\overline{)24}$ (iii) $6(\ )=24$

(iv) $24 \div 6$ (v) $6\underline{)24}$

Figure 10

## Long multiplication

The necessity for long multiplication is arguably a thing of the past since the evidence is overwhelming that most adults use a calculator to perform this type of calculation. However, insofar as it is still taught in school, the greater the variety of methods the children are encouraged to develop to perform this operation the better.

### Area/squared paper method

Take a piece of squared paper. Draw out a rectangle with sides equal in length to the two numbers being multiplied, so a 24 × 17 gives a rectangle 24 squares long by 17 squares wide. Divide the rectangle into tens and units (Figure 11). This gives 4 smaller rectangles within the larger one. At the same time write the problem thus: (20 + 4) × (10 + 7). Now calculate or count the areas of each of the smaller rectangles. This can be written as: (20 + 4) × (10 + 7). Add together the areas of all the mini-rectangles to obtain the answer: 200 + 140 + 40 + 28 = 408.

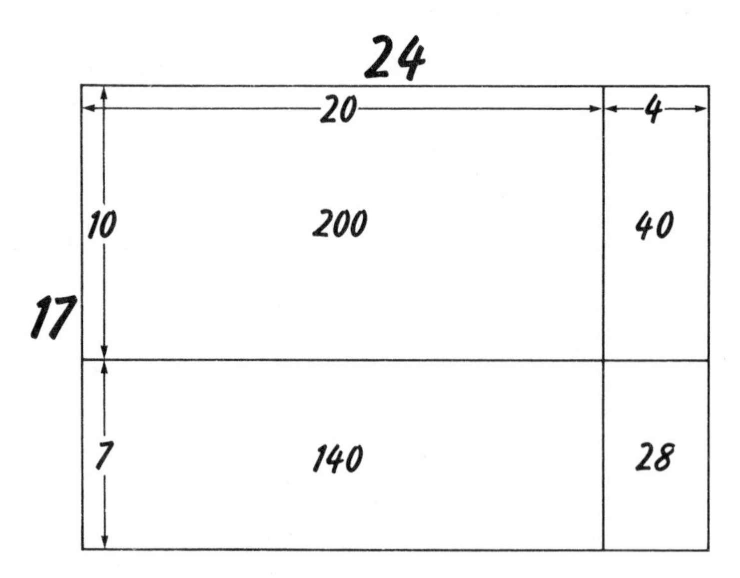


Figure 11

The advantages of this method are that it is easily and practically demonstrated and that it forms a perfect grounding for algebraic multiplication of brackets later: $(3 + x) \times (4 + x)$. Also, place value errors rarely occur since the splitting of the numbers into their tens and units at the start demonstrates that the 2 in 24 is (2 × 10) not 2, and so many mistakes are avoided.

There is an almost infinite variety of different algorithms for performing long multiplication. Children can be encouraged to develop their own: doubling up; multiplying by 10 then subtracting or adding; repeatedly adding up, etc. The calculator is useful – even where long multiplication is being taught as a necessary skill in adult life – as a means of checking answers and occasionally providing assistance with the intermediate stages of the process (e.g. 20 × 10).

## Long division

Long division is as outdated as long multiplication in terms of its usefulness in everyday life. Most people have recourse to calculators in order to perform such operations. It is therefore increasingly difficult to justify the teaching of such algorithms in school. However, children can still be helped to develop strategies for solving problems through long division and should be asked to perform these calculations only when they arise in the context of other work.

The method now encouraged for long division is an extension of the repeated subtraction mentioned earlier. Thus 384 ÷ 13 can be approached as in Figure 12 (overleaf).

The first question posed is how much can I give out of my £384 to each of the 13 people? Can I afford to give them all £10? If I do so I will have used up £10 × 13 = £130 and I will have £254 left. I can now afford to give another £10 note all round and I am then left with £124. I can now try giving out £5 which will use up half of £130, £65, leaving £59. I can now give out 13 lots of £1, leaving £46, and the same again leaving £33 and again leaving £20 and once again leaving £7 so I have finally given out £10 + £10 + £5 + £1 + £1 + £1 + £1 to each of 13 people (£29) and I am left with £7.

As stated above it is not recommended that long multiplication and division be taught now as algorithms in school. However, in circumstances which leave a teacher no option, a variety of different strategies can be suggested. It is important that the methods taught can and must form links with the algebra the children will be tackling in secondary school and must help to develop the concepts involved.

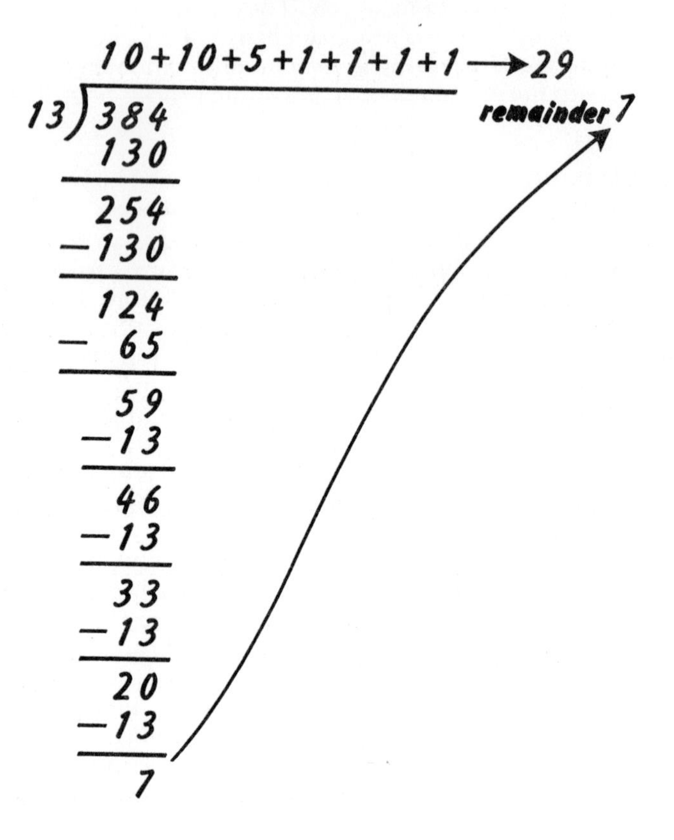
384÷13
10+10+5+1+1+1+1 → 29
13)384
130
254
−130
124
− 65
59
−13
46
−13
33
−13
20
−13
7
remainder 7

Figure 12

# 6

# Number investigations and patterns

Mathematical investigations develop certain skills. They often involve the child in solving a problem and this will mean co-operative work rather than individual competitive work. Working in this way helps the child to acquire the ability to listen to other people, to allow others to be wrong, to offer suggestions and test them out.

Investigations necessarily entail that children collectively acquire, sort and classify data, then hypothesize, test and predict on the basis of that data. They involve a high degree of organization. In what order must the data be amassed to be certain that none is missed? How should it be arranged so as to make sense in the context of a particular investigation?

Children must develop logical and hypothetical modes of thinking ('What if . . .'?). They must learn to test their hypotheses and revise them in the light of further information.

Finally they must seek to demonstrate their discoveries and to present and explain them in ways that other people can understand. Occasionally a child may want to prove a theorem and will succeed in finding a mathematical means of accomplishing a proof.

Investigations enliven and enrich a primary classroom. They form an essential part of all areas in the curriculum but they are particularly crucial in mathematics because the sort of thought processes which they involve are especially relevant to the study of this subject. The ability to think logically, to hypothesize, to predict, to demonstrate and to prove are all vital parts of the process of developing mathematical thinking.

## Investigations involving the use of a calculator

The usefulness of the calculator in the primary classroom has already been discussed in chapter 4. The calculator can be used as a teaching aid like Multilink or Dienes blocks, or as a means of performing necessary but difficult computations quickly and efficiently. Naturally, practice with the calculator will also develop children's skill in using it. Investigations involving the use of the calculator often fulfil all these purposes.

Much is said nowadays concerning the use of investigations as a part of the mathematics curriculum. Investigations such as those involving the use of the calculator are usually best done in small groups or pairs so that the children can discuss things as they work.

These investigations can sometimes be frustrating for children, especially if they do not seem to be getting anywhere. It is therefore a good idea for the teacher to come prepared with some 'pointers' as to possible solutions, and an awareness of the routes which lead straight to a dead end.

Here are some suggestions of investigations with a calculator.

a) How old is Wilf if he has lived exactly one million minutes? Is it possible for him to live this long? How old is someone who has lived a million seconds? Or a million hours? Work out your age in days, not forgetting leap years. How many minutes are there in a year, a decade, a century? Will the calculator show the answer to this last question or is the answer too large?

b) You are allowed to press only the keys 3, 7, +, and =. Which numbers under 20 can be obtained? What happens if two other numbers are chosen? What happens if two even numbers are used? Suppose the operation is varied from + to −? Experiment using different combinations.

c) Given the layout of a sum as in Figure 1, slot the numbers 1, 2, 3, 4, 5, into the boxes in such a way as to obtain the largest answer possible. Is it possible to rewrite the sum so as to obtain an even higher product?

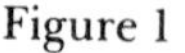

Figure 1

d) Choose any three digits (e.g. 5, 6, 8). Repeat them to obtain a 6–digit number (568568). Divide this number by 11 and by 7. What happens? Try another 3–digit number. Why does this work?

e) Enter any number (7356). Re-arrange the digits (5673). Find the difference between the two numbers. Divide by 9. Try this again using a different number. What happens? Is it possible to work out why?

f) Using exactly four 4s in any combination make all the numbers from 0 to 10. For example, $0 = 44 - 44$.

g) Number chains. Choose any starting number. If it is even, divide by 2. If it is odd, multiply by 3 and add 1. Continue this process for as long as possible. Try another starting number. Does the same thing always happen? Do some numbers work faster than others? Could you predict which numbers will work fastest? Do all numbers work?

h) Consecutive numbers. Some numbers can be written as the sum of consecutive whole numbers (e.g. $15 = 7 + 8$, $9 = 4 + 5$, $12 = 3 + 4 + 5$). Can all numbers be written in this way? Is there any difference between odd and even numbers in this connection?

(i) Chain letters. Annie receives a letter asking her to send a picture postcard to the top name on a list and a letter to each of 5 friends. She is to take the top name off the list and add her own name at the bottom. This is called a chain letter. Susie started this chain off and put her own name at the top of the list and 5 of her friends below. By the time the letter reaches Annie, Susie's fifth friend is at the top of the list. If everyone follows the instructions how many postcards does Susie's fifth friend receive? What percentage of friends must follow the rules for her to receive over 100 cards?

j) Annie has a number of marbles and she sorts them into piles. When she sorts them into piles of 3 she has 1 marble left over. When she sorts them into piles of 4 she has 2 left over. If she sorts them into piles of 5 she has 3 left over. How many marbles does Annie have? Is there more than one answer to this problem?

## Visual patterns and number investigations

Here are some suggestions:

a) The milk crate problem. A milk crate has 24 spaces arranged as 6 rows of 4. The task is to arrange 18 milk bottles in the crate in such a way that every row and every column has an even number of bottles in it. What happens if you start with a crate of 36 spaces in 9 rows of 4 and try to fit in 28 bottles?

b) How many squares can be found on a 3 × 3 chess board? What about a 4 × 4 board, a 5 × 5 board? Is there a pattern? Predict how many squares there will be on a 10 × 10 board.

c) Using a chess board arrange 8 queens in such a way that no queen takes any other queen. There is more than one arrangement of this. Can you find them all? On a 4 × 4 board can 4 queens be arranged so that they are all safe? How many arrangements are possible in this case? What about a 5 × 5 board? Is it possible to get any predictions?

d) A perfect number is a number which is the sum of all its factors. Which are the first four perfect numbers? What do they all have in common? Is this always going to be true?

e) How many different arrangements are possible using 5 Multilink cubes joined face to face. In this investigation it is usually best to start with 3 Multilink and work out how many possible arrangements there are, then progress to 4 and so on. This forces a structure on to the organization of the data and it also gives the start to the pattern which might emerge if 6 Multilink arrangements were to be attempted. Children always enjoy this investigation and it brings together a number of different topic areas: shape; symmetry and rotations; number patterns; differences. The pattern which does emerge is difficult to find and the sorting and classification of the shapes once 6 or 7 Multilink cubes are involved in each arrangement are complex. Although this is a demanding investigation which could involve some fairly high level mathematics, it is also one which can be done quite successfully by top infant children. Such a group will obviously not take the investigation very far but they will learn how best to sort and organize their data so as to see how many shapes they have and whether they have them all. They will also have to discuss the symmetry aspects of the exercise in order to find out which ones to 'count' and which ones not to 'count'.

f) Dividing a rectangle. Draw a rectangle or oblong on squared paper. Draw in a diagonal. Count how many squares are intersected by the diagonal. Now try a different size rectangle. Is there a pattern? Is it possible to predict for any given rectangle exactly how many squares will be cut by the diagonal? This investigation can be made or broken by the care and clarity with which the data is organized. The results, if not tabulated, soon become unmanageable and any patterns there may be in the numbers are lost.

g) Snowflakes. In order to do this investigation large quantities of squared and isometric paper are required. Colour one square (or triangle) in the middle of the paper. Choose a new colour and shade any square (or triangle) which is touching that square (or triangle) by exactly one side. With a third colour shade any square touching these new squares by only one side. Continue to colour squares so that at each stage any new square touches the growing snowflake by exactly and only one side. Keep a note of how many squares are coloured in each colour (Figure 2).

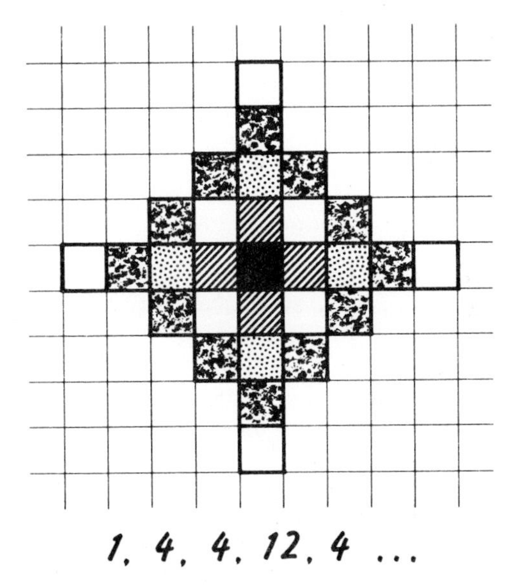


Figure 2

This investigation is exceedingly visual and once the pattern starts to emerge it seems clear from the colours how it will progress. However, as the children discover, it is not so simple and as the snowflake pattern proceeds it becomes clear that to make any real, long-term predictions requires a great deal of information. But the investigation produces some of the most spectacular displays of any investigation suitable for the primary classroom. It is also a peaceful and relaxing task to collect all the data by colouring in all the layers of squares or triangles.

A variation on this involves using isometric or hexagonal paper and colouring regular hexagons applying the same rules. This is much harder as after about three rounds of colouring it will be necessary to make a choice as to which hexagons to colour. The same is true of a diamond snowflake on triangular paper.

h) Police patrol. Using squared, dotted paper draw a variety of squares and oblongs. These squares and oblongs must be patrolled by police who may patrol one square in any direction radiating from their positions in the centre of a cross (Figure 3).

The idea is to position the police so as to use the minimum number of police to patrol any given rectangle. Thus a 6 × 4 rectangle requires at least 12 patrollers to cover every street. How many police are required to patrol a 6 × 2 rectangle, a 6 × 3 rectangle, a 6 × 5 rectangle, etc? Is it possible to make general predictions? Are squares different?

Once again this investigation draws on a number of different topic areas – number patterns, shape, symmetry – and develops a number of different strategies including the necessity to record, organize and tabulate results.

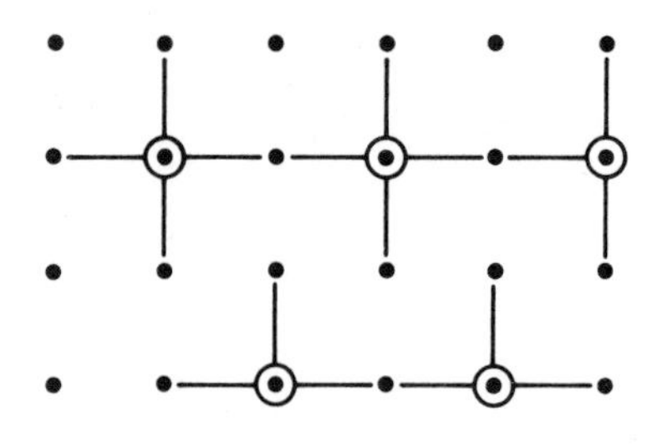

*each policeman may patrol up to 4 'streets'*

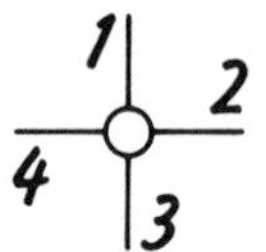


Figure 3

## Investigations in the number square, tables square and number spiral

The use of the number square from 0 – 99, the tables square and the number spiral in investigations makes visual what can be rather abstract and remote number properties and relationships.

**Number squares**

The uses of the 0 – 99 square have been explained in chapters 4 and 5. However, allowing children to invent and investigate their own patterns and squares can not only familiarize them with numbers but also lead to some quite interesting discoveries.

(*i*) Inventing new squares. Children can be encouraged to investigate ways of writing the numbers in other squares: a 7 × 7 square or a 9 × 9 square (Figure 4). They can then try colouring the different multiples (every even number, every third number, etc.) and see what patterns they make on different squares. The investigation of the patterns can be done in a structured way: Do the multiples of 3 make the same pattern on a 3 × 3 or on a 6 × 6 square that the multiples of 4 make on a 4 × 4 or a 8 × 8 square?

| 1 | 2 | 3 | 4 | 5 | 6 | 7 |
|---|---|---|---|---|---|---|
| 8 | 9 | 10 | 11 | 12 | 13 | 14 |
| 15 | 16 | 17 | 18 | 19 | 20 | 21 |
| 22 | 23 | 24 | 25 | 26 | 27 | 28 |
| 29 | 30 | 31 | 32 | 33 | 34 | 35 |
| 36 | 37 | 38 | 39 | 40 | 41 | 42 |
| 43 | 44 | 45 | 46 | 47 | 48 | 49 |

| 0 | 1 | 2 | 3 | 4 | 5 | 6 | 7 | 8 |
|---|---|---|---|---|---|---|---|---|
| 9 | 10 | 11 | 12 | 13 | 14 | 15 | 16 | 17 |
| 18 | 19 | 20 | 21 | 22 | 23 | 24 | 25 | 26 |
| 27 | 28 | 29 | 30 | 31 | 32 | 33 | 34 | 35 |
| 36 | 37 | 38 | 39 | 40 | 41 | 42 | 43 | 44 |
| 45 | 46 | 47 | 48 | 49 | 50 | 51 | 52 | 53 |
| 54 | 55 | 56 | 57 | 58 | 59 | 60 | 61 | 62 |
| 63 | 64 | 65 | 66 | 67 | 68 | 69 | 70 | 71 |
| 72 | 73 | 74 | 75 | 76 | 77 | 78 | 79 | 80 |

Figure 4

(*ii*) Drawing patterns on squares. Children can investigate the patterns they can make on different squares by colouring different numbers according to a variety of rules. For example, arrange the numbers from 0 – 35 on a 6 × 6 square. Colour all the numbers with a 2 in them. How many will be coloured? Then colour the number 35. The children can, by experimenting, make their own number pictures. They can be encouraged to predict, for example, how many little squares they will shade if they colour every number with a 4 in it on a 7 × 7 square. This question is really a place value question since, in order to answer it, the child must think where the 4s will occur.

(*iii*) With older children, squares can be drawn showing the numbers in different bases. This gives a sense of how the base we work in affects the patterns which emerge. The easiest for children is start with base 7 and think of it as weeks. Thus arranging the numbers in 7s gives a grid where each row represents 7 days or a week.
(*iv*) The children can use a number square to discover all the prime numbers up to 100. This is known mathematically as Eratosthenes' sieve. The children cross out all the multiples of 2 on the square, then all the multiples of 3 and so on until all the multiples of every prime number up to 10 have been crossed out. (To operate Erotosthenes' sieve up to any number $x$, the multiples of primes up to and including the square root of $x$ must be crossed out.) The numbers remaining not crossed out on the square must be prime.

## Tables square

A similar approach can be taken to the tables square as was applied to the numbers square. The tables square is always harder for the children to investigate because each number is itself a product and therefore must first have been obtained by multiplication.

(*i*) The children can investigate mini-tables squares (Figure 5) and maxi-tables squares (above 10). These smaller squares are themselves portions of the usual tables and that itself comes to be seen as a portion of an infinitely large tables square. The children can build up the squares until they are doing their 16 and 27 times tables! Here they may use a calculator to check some products.

| 1 | 2 | 3 | 4 | 5 | 6 |
|---|---|---|---|---|---|
| 2 | 4 | 6 | 8 | 10 | 12 |
| 3 | 6 | 9 | 12 | 15 | 18 |
| 4 | 8 | 12 | 16 | 20 | 24 |
| 5 | 10 | 15 | 20 | 25 | 30 |
| 6 | 12 | 18 | 24 | 30 | 36 |

Figure 5

(*ii*) Investigate the patterns, if any, made by shading square numbers, cubed numbers (1, 8, 27 . . .), triangular numbers (1, 3, 6,

10 . . .), on the tables square. Are all the triangular numbers under 100 on the tables square? Are there any prime triangular numbers above 3?

### Number spirals

Where younger children are concerned, the benefits to be gained from simply playing with writing numbers in different spiral arrangements are enormous. They develop a familiarity with the numbers as a series and a sense of the infinity of that series – a difficult concept for small children. They can investigate the various properties of numbers (even/odd, square, etc.) which are exposed by the different arrangements using both square and isometric paper. Children can invent their own number spirals and colour their own patterns (Figure 6).

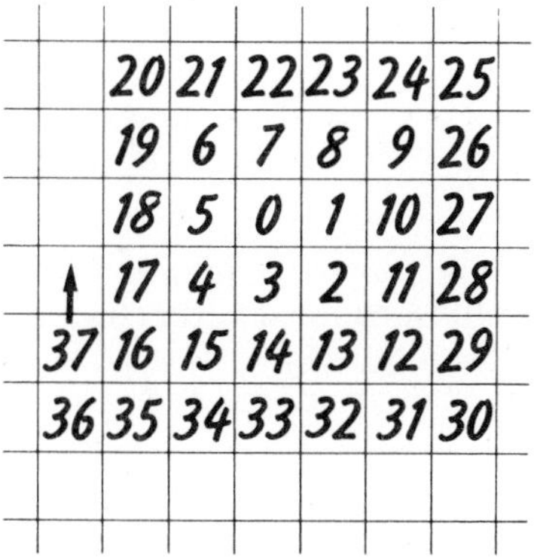

| | 20 | 21 | 22 | 23 | 24 | 25 |
|---|---|---|---|---|---|---|
| | 19 | 6 | 7 | 8 | 9 | 26 |
| | 18 | 5 | 0 | 1 | 10 | 27 |
| ↑ | 17 | 4 | 3 | 2 | 11 | 28 |
| 37 | 16 | 15 | 14 | 13 | 12 | 29 |
| 36 | 35 | 34 | 33 | 32 | 31 | 30 |

Figure 6

## Magic squares, Fibonacci's sequence, Pascal's triangle

The history of mathematics yields an almost infinite number of ideas which are worth investigating but magic squares, the Fibonacci sequence and Pascal's triangle are each outstanding both in terms of their usefulness in stimulating thought and mathematics in the primary classroom and in the impact they have had historically.

## Magic squares

The story is that the first magic square appeared on the back of a turtle which crawled up out of the Yang-tze river in China. The square on the back of the turtle looked like this (Figure 7).

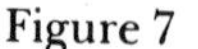

Figure 7

All the rows and columns on this square add up to 15 and the diagonals also add up to 15. A more recent square was produced by the artist Dürer in 1514 (Figure 8).

| | | | |
|---|---|---|---|
| 16 | 3 | 2 | 13 |
| 5 | 10 | 11 | 8 |
| 9 | 6 | 7 | 12 |
| 4 | 15 | 14 | 1 |

Figure 8

This square has the date in the middle of the bottom row. Magic squares used to be credited with magical properties and were used as prophylactics in the Middle Ages to ward off the plague. They were worn on the wrist and put on doors.

Children can experiment with magic squares, adding them up and discovering the patterns that exist within them. For example, in Figure 8 the four squares in each corner also add up to the same as the diagonals, columns and rows.

New magic squares can be generated by adding a constant to each figure. Children can thus make their own magic square.

## The Fibonacci sequence and Pascal's triangle

Both the Fibonacci sequence which is obtained by adding the first two numbers to get the third (Figure 9), and Pascal's triangle (Figure 10) can be used for generating lots of fascinating mathematical patterns and as the basis of much useful extended mathematics for the top juniors. These famous historical pieces of mathematics can be found very clearly explored in *Discovering Mathematical Thinking* by Lorraine Mottershead (Blackwell).

1, 1, 2, 3, 5, 8, 13, 21, 34, 55 . . . etc

Figure 9

```
            1
          1   1
        1   2   1
      1   3   3   1
    1   4   6   4   1
  1   5  10  10   5   1
1   6  15  20  15   6   1
                      etc
```

Figure 10

Some of the most magical properties of mathematics are discovered when children start playing with numbers and doing relatively open-ended investigations. The HMI Document recommends that children should be enabled to see the intrinsic beauty of mathematics. Investigations can often be the means of their doing just this.

# 7

# Length, area, volume and capacity

## Length

The structured teaching of length must begin by introducing the basic concept of comparison. It is sometimes assumed in the teaching of measures that children possess basic concepts already. This assumption is dangerous, especially since the lack of such concepts in this particular topic area can often remain masked until much later when the child is required to think through complex ideas rather than simply copy a practice or skill.

### Comparison

Children must be encouraged to compare lengths. It is vital that the *relativity* of length is always kept in mind by the teacher. Thus it is no good having a 'long box' and a 'short box' or designing a worksheet asking the child to draw '5 long things' and '5 short things'. A dachshund is long compared with a hampster but short compared with a python! There must always be a basis for comparison if we are to encourage children to describe certain things as long and others as short. Children must begin by comparing directly – that is, matching the things to be compared against each other. Indirect comparisons – for example, comparing by the use of a measure (the table is 6 pencils long, the cupboard is 5 pencils long) – will come later.

Much of this initial length work will be language work. The children must be encouraged to talk about things they have seen and touched. To start with, their language will be rather vague, involving words like *bigger than, smaller than, little, large, wide, narrow, thin*, but gradually, with much encouragement and guidance, the children's vocabulary will become more precise and particular words will be chosen to fit the appropriate comparisons. This involves a great deal of work which will most probably be oral rather than written. Stories must be read and discussion encouraged. Some writing or drawing may be necessary at times as a means of recording.

Some suggestions for activities include:

(*i*) Comparisons in the classroom. Children are given, or choose, an object on which to base their comparisons of length. They can all make this themselves if required. A mouse cut out of felt and with a string tail makes an excellent example (Figure 1). Then the children are encouraged to make a collection of things which are 'longer than mouse' and another set which are 'shorter than mouse'. The comparisons are always made directly, and their work can be recorded as pictures, writing or even on a worksheet, if required.

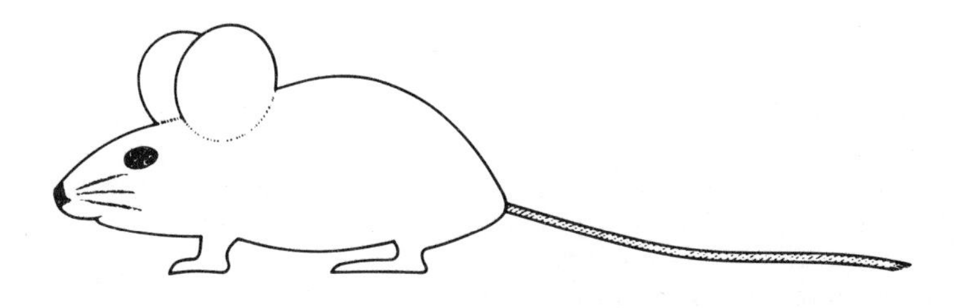

Figure 1

(*ii*) Markers on the door. Three different coloured strips are stuck horizontally on the door, one above the other at different heights so that most of the children will measure between the first and second strips, some will be below the first strip or above the second and only adults will be above the third (see picture on page 78). The children write their names on brightly coloured labels and stick them on the door at the level of their height. Each set of names is appropriately labelled 'taller than the green strip and shorter than the red strip', or 'taller than the red strip but shorter than the blue strip'. The children love to put their names on the door and much useful mathematical language arises out of their actions. Comments about the relative heights of different children will be made and these can be checked by means of a direct comparison, standing the children back to back. All the comparisons here are direct, no measures are involved and the completed sets make a lively display. Remember to include the teacher's height!

*Writing names between strips at different heights*

**Conservation of length**

The idea of conservation of length, that is, that the length of an object does not change because it is moved, has always proved difficult for children to grasp. They are inclined to think that the object which 'juts out at one end' is the longest (Figure 2).

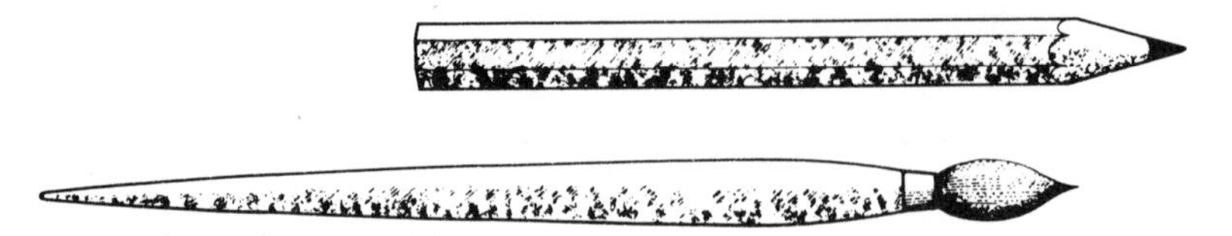

Figure 2

So when comparing two lengths it is essential that we establish from the start the concept of a 'base-line'. For example, if two children are comparing the length of their feet, they must put their heels against the same line. To encourage the notion of a base-line it is sometimes useful if, when comparing the heights of two children, the smaller of the two is given high-heeled shoes or a low chair to stand on. This will provoke the whole class into a protest of, 'It's not fair, she's really taller but you've cheated and made him taller'. That protest of, 'It's not fair . . .' is what having a base-line is all about, keeping the comparison 'fair'. From this we can develop the idea that if we move things away from the base-line the comparison is 'not fair' and they must be lined up. Then it is a small step to making it understood that when an object is moved to be lined up on a base-line its length does not alter.

**Measurement as repeating a unit**

All measurement involves, in one way or another, repeating a unit. In the case of length it is relatively easy to get this idea across to small children since they can easily handle objects of different lengths.

Too great an emphasis on written recording throughout these early stages can be counter-productive since it can put children off and weaken the experience of handling things.

(*i*) Making up a length. Children can make up a length using a number of smaller objects (Figure 3). This encourages the idea that one length can be broken down into a number of smaller 'pieces'.

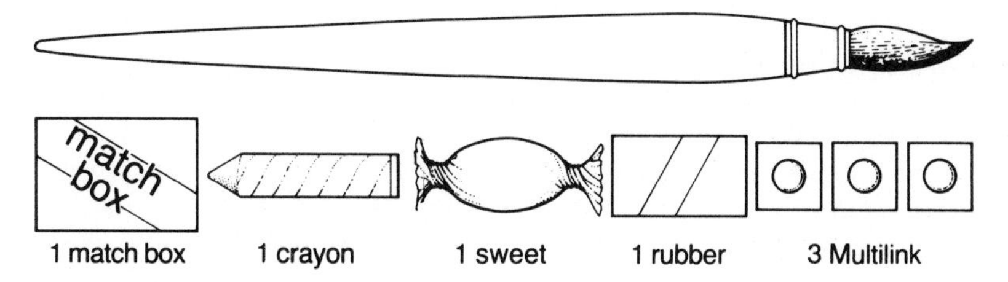


Figure 3

(*ii*) Making up a length using a non-uniform unit. Children can move on to making up a length using a repetition of one particular object (Figure 4). This can then form the basis for comparisons. A table is 7 crayons long and the cupboard is 10 crayons long. Which is the longer? The children are moving from direct comparisons to indirect comparisons by means of a unit. Many children will have difficulty if only 1 crayon is used and put down 7 times along the length of the table. To start with at least, there need to be 7 crayons laid end-to-end along the table so that both the matching and the

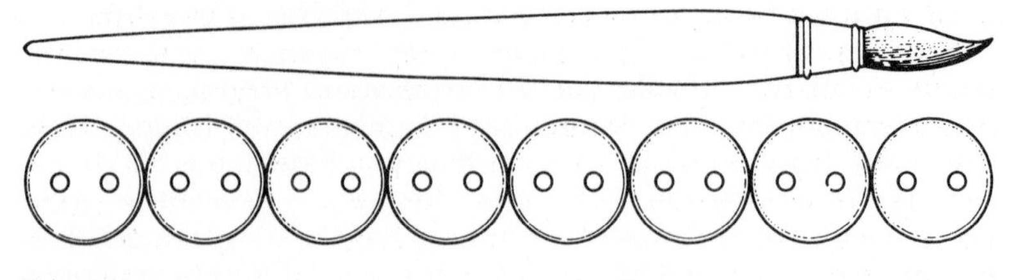

Figure 4

repetition are clear to the child. Children must develop the habit of first estimating the number of units an object measures. This encourages good judgement of length and is useful experience for later on.

## Units

When developing the concept of measurement as repeating a unit we use the following general strategy. The strategy does not apply simply to length but is applicable to measures more generally.

| *Children must experience* | *Explanation* | *Examples* |
| --- | --- | --- |
| 1) Non-uniform, non-standard units | These are units which are not exactly the same but vary according to certain factors. Therefore, a bed made to be 10 handspans long will vary according to the person who measured and made it. | Crayons, pencils, straws, biscuits, sweets, paintbrushes, body measurements, including handspans, cubits, paces. |
| 2) Uniform, non-standard units | These are units which do not vary in length and therefore do provide a repeated unit as a basis for measuring and comparing. | Multilink, Unifix, Cuisenaire Rods, playing cards, match-boxes, marbles. |
| 3) Standard units | It is accepted that we teach the SI units but a child who has had plenty of practical experience of measurements as repeating a unit will have no difficulty in thinking in any measure, whether it is hand-spans, Unifix, centimetres or inches. | SI units – metres, centimetres, decimetres, millimetres, etc. Inches, feet, yards, etc. |

Children must be encouraged to measure with as many different sorts of repeating unit as possible. They can measure their own height in 'plastic figures' and compare their heights using the measurements obtained: Sammy is 10 'plastic figures' high, Joanna is 9 'plastic figures' high; so Sammy is taller than Joanna. They should be allowed to choose their own unit whenever possible so that they develop the concept of an appropriate unit. Thus they can measure a box in Multilink or Unifix, the table in match-boxes and the length of the classroom in straws, first estimating on each occasion the likely number of units. Realizing what is and is not a sensible unit in any particular circumstance is a necessary skill to acquire.

When it comes to measuring, children should progress through the following stages:

- direct comparisons
- indirect comparisons using non-uniform measures laid end to end
- indirect comparisons using non-uniform measures – one unit repeated many times
- measuring using uniform units
- becoming familiar with standard units and their 'feel'
- measuring in standard units
- computations involving measurements in standard units.

Before the children come to measure using standard SI units they should have time to become quite used to the 'size' and 'feel' of these units.

(*i*) They can make their own decimetre strip (Figure 5) and then use it in exactly the same way as they have used the other uniform units, to measure and compare things around them. The decimetre is a very useful unit because it is just the right size for the children to handle easily. A centimetre is too small to be an appropriate unit for measuring desks, cupboards, etc. to the sort of accuracy appropriate to this age and a metre is too big to be useful in this context.

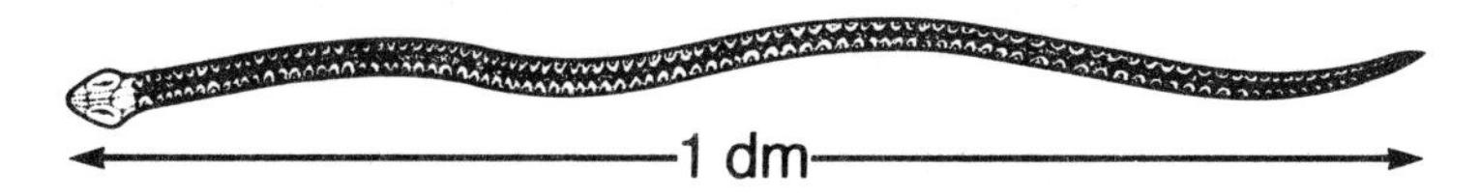


Figure 5

(*ii*) Children can find out their various body measurements in SI units. This will involve making a record of their handspan, their waist measurement, their wrist circumference, the length of their foot, their head circumference, and so on, in SI units. They should always be encouraged to start by making an estimate the length they are about to measure. Some body measurements provide a very useful means of estimating the length of something: the distance across a little finger is about one centimetre, so the length of something can be quite accurately estimated by placing the little finger repeatedly along it. The average handspan is usually about 20–22 cm in women and 22–25 cm in men. Measuring parts of the body also leads to a better 'feel' for the units involved.

### Measuring 'round' – circumference and perimeter

It is relatively common for older children to confuse perimeter and area. Such a confusion betrays a lack of practical experience in the infant and junior school. Children must be encouraged to measure 'round' things right from the start. They can place a strip of paper round their waist to make a belt or round their head to make a headband. The paper can be stretched out and measured with either standard or non-standard units. As always the children should estimate the length first. Getting curly pieces of string and asking children to estimate their length is a useful way of emphasizing that length does not mean only the measurement of straight lines (Figure 6).

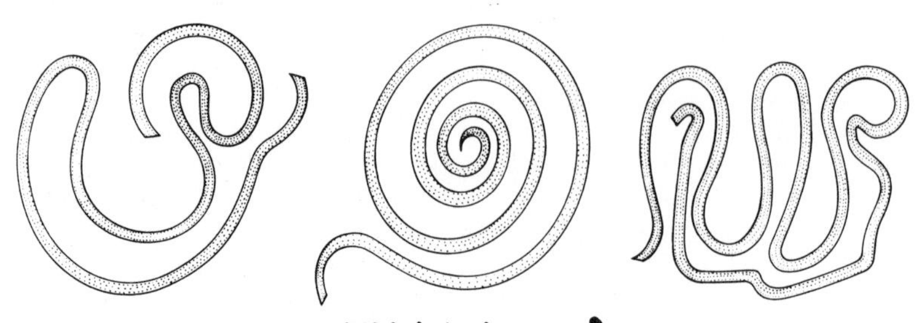


Figure 6

## Area

### Preliminary area work

It is always a mistake to think that length must be introduced before area and that area is therefore a junior topic. Area should be introduced as 'covering' a surface with a repeated unit. As with length, that unit at the preliminary stages and even a little further on, does not have to be either uniform or standard.

It helps if the children get used to covering different surfaces with a variety of different objects, both uniform and non-uniform. It is, of course, important to emphasize that the covering must be complete (i.e. that the units must tesselate). So a child could cover a book with match-boxes or a table with books and count them up. At this early stage, even in recording, it is not essential to use the word 'area'. '15 books covered the table but only 10 covered the top of the cupboard' is a quite adequate way to record the activity.

**Tesselations**

All work in tesselations helps develop the idea of area as covering and measurement of area as repeating a unit covering a surface. Thus it helps to make the notion of 2-D measurement more concrete.

(*i*) Early work on tesselations. This should include discussions on shapes which tesselate and those which do not. The children can experiment with solid shapes – not just regular ones – cut out of cardboard and see if they tesselate; they can make mosaics out of fabric and paper. They should be encouraged to try those shapes which do not tesselate, such as circles and ovals, as well as those that do. It is worth while obtaining some prints of tesselation patterns by the artist Escher, so that the children can see some really beautiful and original examples of irregular tesselations.

(*ii*) Cut-and-put tesselations. This way of doing more complex tesselation work, made famous by the artist Escher, is more suitable for upper juniors but it can be simplified and used with top infants or lower juniors. The children cut out a shape which they know tesselates. Then they cut a piece out of one side and mount it on to the opposite side (Figure 7).

This can be repeated if a very complex and irregular shape is required. The children can then either use their shape as a template and draw round it or they can cut out a number of identical shapes from coloured paper or fabric and make a stunning tesselation collage.

(*iii*) Tesselating polygons. Children can investigate regular polygons to discover which ones tesselate.

What is the smallest number of sides you can have on a regular polygon which tesselates?
Which other regular polygons tesselate?

Is there a pattern as to which ones do and which ones do not?
Which common irregular polygons tesselate?
What about inverted polygons (i.e. polygons with one or more angles greater than 180°)?

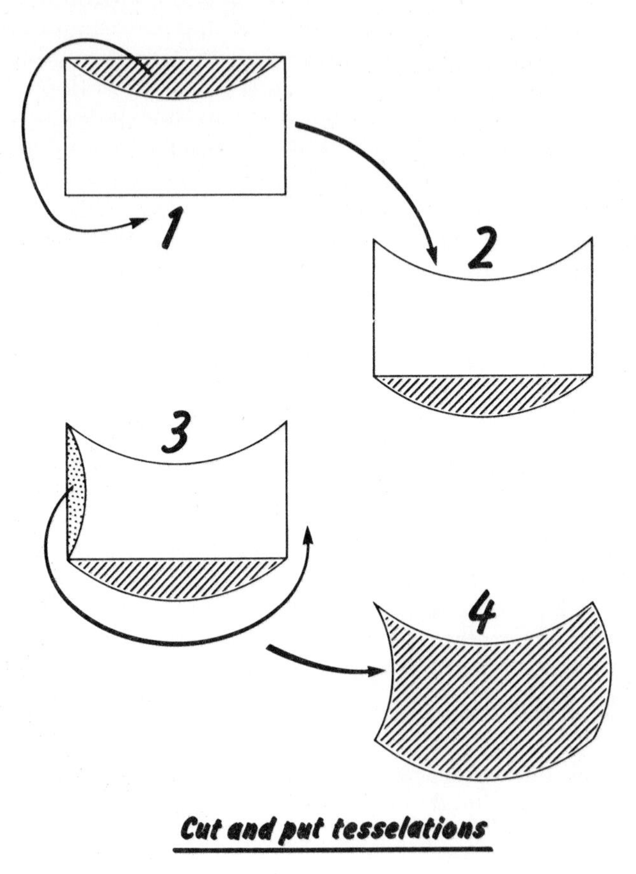


Figure 7

**Standard units in area**

Although the pattern of working through non-uniform/uniform, non-standard/standard units is the same for area as it is for length, it is even more vital that the early stages of area work are not rushed and that children are not introduced too early to formulae like 'length x breadth', or $\pi r^2$. Children need start by doing a lot of work drawing shapes around their hand, their foot, a piece of bread or any unusual shape on squared paper, hexagonal paper and isometric printed paper.

Once they have mastered counting the squares or other shapes, most children will short-cut the process of counting all the squares in the middle by realizing that, where possible, the area will be found by counting the number of squares in each row and then counting the number of rows and multiplying (Figure 8). Even on an asymmetric shape the children will count the rectangle in the middle by saying that, 'it is 10 rows of 15 squares', and then adding on the 'bumps' around the rectangle. Formulae should never be introduced to children until top junior or lower secondary level, when it is certain that most children will be sufficiently familiar with the concept of area not to start assuming that area is a measure of length – a special sort of perimeter or circumference.

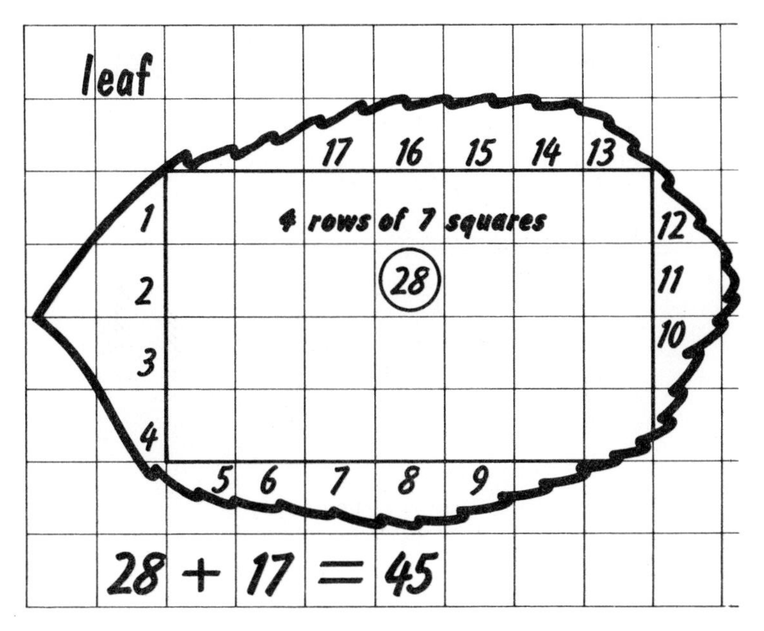


Figure 8

**Conservation of area**

As with length, conservation can prove a difficult concept for some children to grasp. A good way of demonstrating it is to collect a load of old packets and boxes and share them out amongst the class. Then ask everyone to make a building using 6 boxes. The building is to be only one storey high with all the boxes touching and is to cover the minimum area possible. The children will work on this until they find that it makes no difference to the area covered if the boxes are shuffled around the table into different arrangements.

Another idea is to 'explode' a gummed paper square. The children take a gummed paper square and cut it into strips, then they arrange the strips and stick them on to contrasting coloured paper in any pattern they like with the proviso that the pieces must touch at least at one corner (Figure 9). This activity makes a lovely display and is very good for demonstrating conservation since the area of the gummed square remains the same whether it is cut into strips or left in one piece.

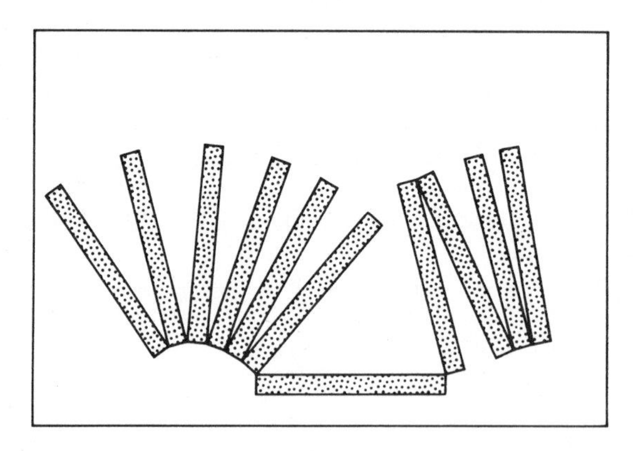

Figure 9

## Volume and capacity

Volume and capacity are often confused and children also have difficulty in separating the volume of an object from its weight. The volume of an object is the amount of space it takes up; the capacity of an object is the amount of space or liquid it holds. Capacity, therefore, is internal volume. Thus the volume of a vacuum flask is the amount of space it takes up in the picnic basket and its capacity is the amount of hot tea it holds. Volume is an abstract concept and very hard for children to grasp because of the 'non-tangibility of volume', that is to say, a particular volume cannot be touched, seen or felt without a container. Thus a litre must be a litre of sand or water or beer and so can only be seen or handled in a container.

### Direct comparison

When learning about volume children need plenty of experience of direct comparison because of the problem of non-tangibility. They need to handle containers and the different materials – water, lentils, sand, rice, beads and buttons – available to fill them. Words like *full, empty, half-full, overflowing,* should be used and these ideas developed through trying out the containers and the materials. It is impossible to overfill with water, but you can have a cup which is 'overfull of sand'.

It is very hard for children to compare the volumes of two different containers directly. For a long time the question, 'Which holds more, A or B?' will mean to a small child, 'In which container is the level of liquid higher?' If a teapot full of water is poured into a slightly smaller jug, the spillage may not be sufficient to cause the child to realize that the teapot is actually bigger, that is, that it will hold more water. It is good practice to encourage children to pour water both from the first container into the second and back again, as the fact that the containers are not of equal volume will show up in the 'not full' container. It takes a lot of practice and structured play before children develop the concept of capacity and become adept at comparing containers.

Once again, as in all work with measures, there is no substitute for practical work. Children simply cannot acquire these concepts by working on paper or with worksheets and the emphasis must be on doing and not on recording.

### Indirect comparisons

Once again the same principles of using non-uniform, non-standard measures to start with apply to volume and capacity and the children should always be asked to estimate first.

(*i*) Measuring volumes. The children can make 'magic potions' by mixing all sorts of strange (non-poisonous!) ingredients (e.g. coloured waters, squash, fizzy drinks, sugar and flavourings). They can be encouraged to measure the amounts of each substance going in – one egg-cup of lemonade, two yogurt pots of pink water, and so on – and to measure the total quantity of potion made. This has easy and obvious links with language work – they can describe exactly how they made the potion, and what happens if you drink it ('It turns you into a cat.'). Both their imaginative writing and their practical knowledge of measuring volume can be improved by such an exercise.

(*ii*) Comparing volumes. Some of the children can fill a set of different containers of different shapes with coloured water (Figure 10). Others can then be invited to place them in order of quantity from most to least full; their orders must be recorded. The task of recording can itself be quite complex, involving symbols or pictures. Next the liquid in each container is measured carefully using an appropriate measure: egg-cup, spoon, yogurt pot, tea cup, etc., and the different sizes recorded:

Teapot – 8 yogurt pots
Milk bottle – 5 yogurt pots
Coca-cola bottle – 4 yogurt pots

Figure 10

This activity also makes a good survey for a block graph, looking at people's estimates and their errors. Even adults find it hard to estimate volume and quite often make wide misjudgements.

## Standard units

SI units must really be left until late in the junior school since volume and capacity are such very abstract notions. When teaching the SI units, a litre is difficult to handle in the classroom because it is always too much water to pour without a spillage, while a millilitre is generally too small to be an appropriate measure. A decilitre, however, makes a very good unit to handle. It fits comfortably into a reasonably small container (yogurt pot) and can be useful for measuring the capacity of bottles, etc.

(*i*) Proving a millilitre = a cubic centimetre (1ml = 1cc).
Press a 5-Colour Factor or Cuisenaire rod or a 5 centi-cube Dienes block into the plasticine to make a hole exactly 5 cc in size. Now fill a

5 ml medicine spoon (available from any chemist), preferably one which says 5 ml on the handle, and carefully tip the liquid into the imprint in the plasticine. The liquid should exactly fill the hole.

(*ii*) Nets. Children can make 'nets' which will fold up to make 3-D shapes (Figure 11). These nets can make a specific volume, a net of a cube where each face measures 10 cm × 10 cm will fold up to give a cube of 1-litre volume.

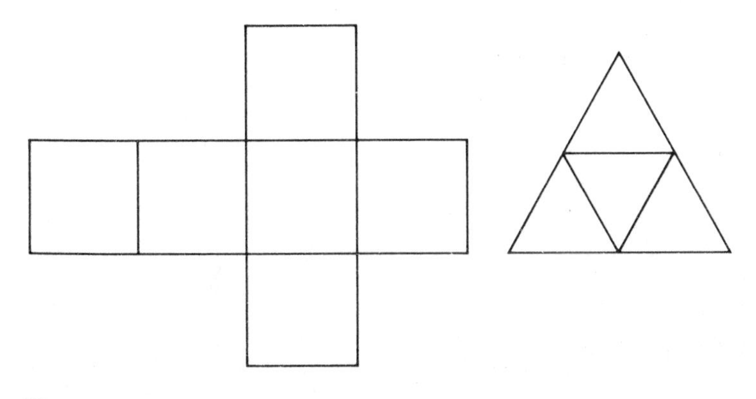

Figure 11

Children can carefully open out small Cornflake packets, cones or toilet rolls to see what shape the net is. They can also invent their own nets.

A suitable investigation for second, third and fourth years juniors involves finding out how many arrangements of 6 squares will make the net of a cube. How do the children order and organize their attempts? Do they know whether they have found them all?

This investigation not only helps to develop the concept of volume and the idea of a net but also gives practice in the essential mathematical skills of ordering, classifying and recording data.

Children must be encouraged to investigate the nets of the more unusual shapes like tetrahedrons, pyramids and prisms.

Nets can be used to make attractive resources. The net of a cube cut out of card and mounted on paper marbled by the children and then varnished can make a spectacular little box.

(*iii*) The marbles in the jar. A popular volume investigation involves filling a jar with marbles and then inviting guesses from the children as to how much of the jar is air and how much is marbles. Estimates range from half marbles to nine-tenths marbles. How to find out poses a real problem for the children who may canvas many methods before alighting on the idea of filling the jar of marbles with water and then pouring the water into another jar of the same shape, leaving the marbles behind in the first jar. It can then be seen how much of the jar was taken up by the space between the marbles.

(*iv*) Volume-capacity difference. The difference between the volume and the capacity of a soda siphon or a vacuum flask can be measured using the technique of displacement. The children measure the capacity in the normal way and then, in order to discover the volume, they must immerse the container in a full trough of water and catch the volume of liquid it displaces. In the case of some containers the volume–capacity difference is remarkable. Try it with a vacuum flask and a hot water bottle.

(*v*) The volume of oxygen in the air. Top juniors are fascinated to realize that we can measure the volume of oxygen burned by a candle. Use a jar containing a candle upturned in a trough of water (Figure 12). The level of the water in the jar is marked at the start of the experiment, then the candle is lit, the jar replaced and as the oxygen burns the water rises inside the jar to replace the oxygen burned. A second mark can be made on the jar at the water-line when the candle goes out having burned up all the oxygen. The jar is then filled to the mark and the volume of oxygen in that jar of air can be measured.

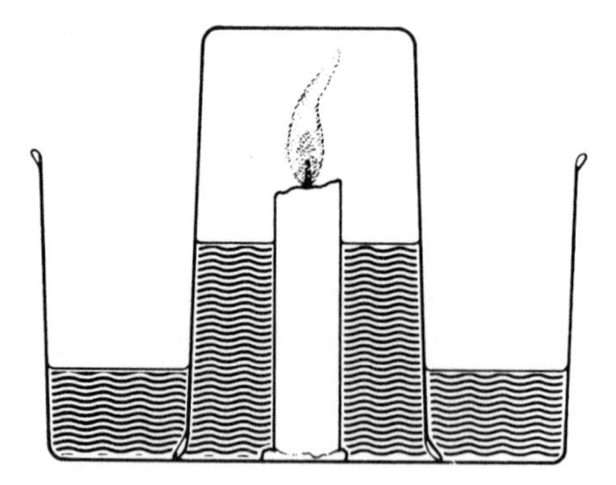

Figure 12

# 8

# Weight, time, money/cost, temperature

## Weight

The topic of weight fits naturally into the primary curriculum. Children, even before they come to school, may have experiences of weighing – helping with cooking, standing on the bathroom scales, watching the baby being weighed at the clinic. But developing a concept of weight can, nonetheless, be quite difficult. Children have to separate the notion of weight from that of size or quantity. They must come to recognize and understand appropriate words and language such as *heavy, light, balanced,* etc. As with all kinds of measurement, children need a large number of practical experiences in order to acquire the concepts involved.

### Direct comparisons

Encourage children to make lots of comparisons. The easiest equipment to use is a balance (Figure 1). By putting one object in one side and another in the other side, the child obtains a direct comparison of their relative weights. Encourage estimation: 'This object looks

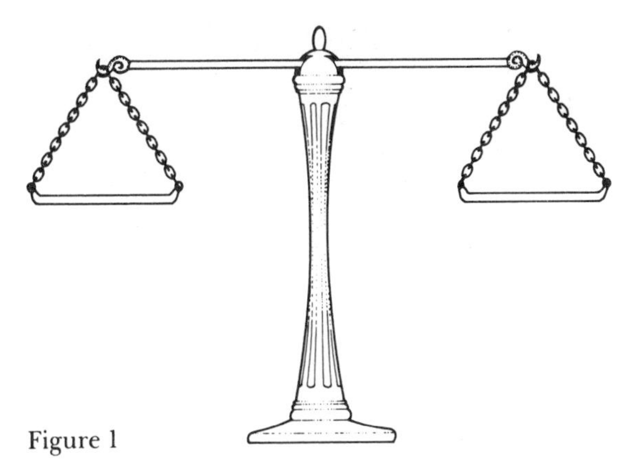

Figure 1

heavier than that one'. Children can become quite skilful at estimating relative weights and trying to find things which are heavier, lighter or the same weight as a pair of scissors. This sort of activity can be very helpful in developing a 'feel' for what weight is.

(*i*) Set children the task of finding several objects lighter or heavier than one specified object. The children must first estimate and decide which objects to use, and then check the weight of each chosen object by putting it on the balance opposite the given object. Once the children have the idea of comparing weights in this way they can be asked to find something *equal* in weight to the given object. This is much more difficult, and the whole idea of balance, has to be acquired through much practical activity and learning by trial and error. This activity involves direct comparison. Once the children have mastered this idea they can go on to develop the notion of a unit of weight.

(*ii*) Children can be asked to find as many different things as possible that are about the same weight but are of very different sizes and shapes. Thus, they may collect a large bundle of paper tissues, a small piece of a heavy metal, a small handful of plastic bricks, one wooden brick, four pencils, and a large bundle of straws. The children can decide for themselves how to check their selection to make sure that they are all the same weight. They must also decide just how accurate they are going to be with their weighing. It is worth mentioning that there is no such thing as completely accurate weighing. Using very sophisticated scientific scales, a reading of an object's weight to several places of decimals can be obtained. The degree of accuracy required will depend on the purpose of the weighing. For cooking, fairly accurate weighing is required, but in a classroom activity like the one outlined above, the weighing does not have to be so precise.

(*iii*) The children can try to balance themselves using a see-saw of some description (the see-saw can be a plank over an upturned school bench if necessary). The children are comparing weights and care must be taken not to make overall comparisons. Thus it is perfectly acceptable to compare two individual children's weight, but not to point out 'Jimmy' as the heaviest boy in the class. At this stage the children are still involved in direct comparison and no units of weight, either arbitrary or uniform, have been introduced.

## Weighing in non-standard units

Once children have grasped the concept of weight, they can make comparisons between different objects by the use of units of weight. These are indirect comparisons – this object weighs 6 units, and that one weighs 9 units, therefore this object is lighter than that object.

(*i*) Take 20 small bricks, such as Multilink, and find 3 things in the classroom which balance them in the scales. Each of these 3 things weighs 20 Multilink, so all 3 are the same weight. This sounds obvious but it is not so to small children.

(*ii*) Weigh one object in a number of different 'units', e.g. a pair of scissors in marbles, in bricks, in new pencils or crayons.

(*iii*) Find the weight of several things in marbles (or any other small object) and write down their respective weights. Make a graph of the results.

(*iv*) A good cake can be made using the old-fashioned recipe: 'The weight of 3 eggs in butter, flour and sugar'. Cream together the butter and sugar, beat in the eggs and stir in the flour (if the flour is plain, add a large teaspoon of baking powder). Bake in 2 sandwich tins for 25 minutes at 375 F. This cake can be flavoured with grated chocolate or cocoa if required. Children can often learn and retain more mathematics when it appears as a part of their ordinary life (and the relevance is immediately obvious to them) than they can when it is presented merely as a textbook subject.

## Introduction of standard units

The use of balances has an obvious advantage when standard units are being introduced. Children can see and handle the weights, whereas with scales, the units have to be read.

(*i*) Using 100 gram weights, find some objects or collections of objects which weigh exactly 100 grams, 200 grams, etc.

(*ii*) Find how many bags of granulated sugar (1 kg) are needed to balance one child's tray. This problem can be approached several ways depending upon the ages and abilities of the children involved. Younger children may require a balance or see-saw in order to balance the tray against the sugar. Older children may weigh first the tray and then one bag on scales and divide to find out how many bags are required.

(*iii*) Cooking almost any recipe requires children to weigh quantities of various things in standard units. It must be remembered that in some cultures, quantities for cooking are measured by volume rather than by weight, and so not all children will be familiar with weighing things as part of the cooking process. However, cooking in the classroom does provide an excellent way of learning about weight in context and it is a far more effective way of studying this topic than any other because it is so practical, because there is an in-built incentive to get the weights right, and because the results can give such pleasure.

(*iv*) More advanced experiments involving weighing, include weighing all the ingredients of a cake before they are amalgamated and cooked, and then weighing them all after they have been cooked. The children can be asked to offer explanations for the difference!

(*v*) A similar activity to the one outlined above involves weighing conkers. Clearly this has to be done at the right time of year; children can collect conkers and bring them into school. These can be subjected to a variety of processes – long slow cooking, short fast cooking, freezing, soaking in water, soaking in oil, etc. They can be weighed before and after these processes. The children can speculate as to the effect each treatment has upon the weight. The conkers can also be tried out as weapons before and after their treatments to discover what effect, if any, the processes to which they have been subjected have had upon their performance in a conker-fight.

(*iv*) A good experiment involving weight to try with middle juniors consists in weighing a loaf of unwrapped bread every day for a week or a fortnight, and watching what happens to its weight. The children are asked to estimate what they think will happen. How much weight the loaf loses depends upon the type of loaf used. A white loaf loses a much greater proportion of its own weight than a brown wholemeal loaf. A separate experiment can be performed to show this, using different types of bread. The results of each day's weighing can be recorded on a graph by the children themselves (Figure 2).

## Different methods of weighing things

(*i*) Simple balance scales have already been mentioned as the most useful means of weighing things in the infant school. There are two types of balances, those which are suspended and those which are balanced. Both types are adjustable, although with the suspended sort this is perhaps easier.

(*ii*) Spring balances are also useful. They emphasize the notion of

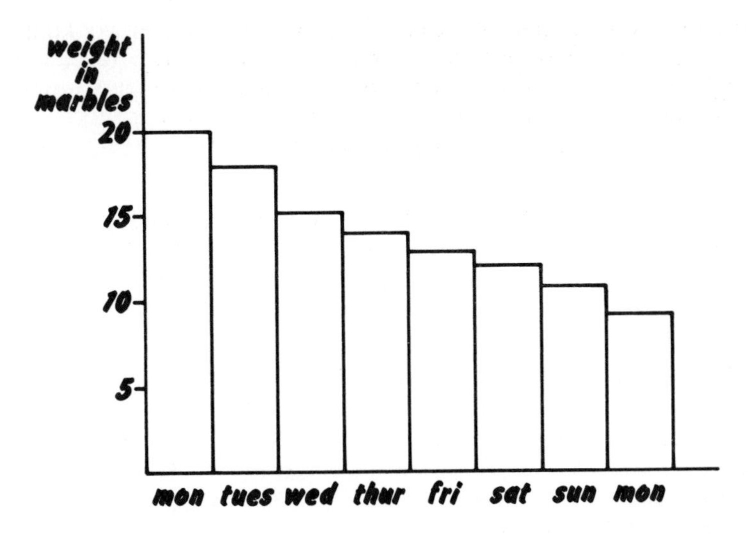


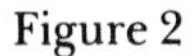
Figure 2

weight as a downwards force, and feeling the pull on a spring balance as it is held in mid-air can really assist the estimation of weight. This type of balance is still used to measure the weight of new-born babies if they are born at home.

(*iii*) Kitchen scales are perhaps the most commonly used type of weighing machine for cooking. Some types nowadays have an adjustable dial so that they can register in imperial or metric units.

(*iv*) Bathroom scales will be familiar to many children who will have seen them at home.

## Time

Time is one of the most difficult measures to teach, because it is intangible and continuous. Children often have some difficulty grasping the notions of 'future' and 'past', and even quite old children can make remarks or ask questions which betray a lack of understanding of these concepts.

### The emphasis on structures – what happens when

There is often pressure on teachers to teach children how to tell the time. But there is no point in a child being able to read off a digital display or even off a clockface if they are still asking questions such as: 'Have I had my dinner yet?' It is essential that children are able to locate what happens when in the course of the day if telling the time is to be a useful skill.

(*i*) Structure the day in terms of the events which take place, roughly speaking, on the hours. This will enable the child to develop a skeleton structure of the day (at 7 o'clock I get up . . . at 8 o'clock I have my breakfast . . . at 9 o'clock I start school . . . etc.). Children can be encouraged to recognize the hours both on the clockface and on the digital watch.

(*ii*) A skeleton structure of the year can also be developed by discussing which months make up the seasons, and when the main religious festivals occur. There are links here with other areas of the curriculum. Indeed, much of the work that the children do on the topic of time will consist of writing or drawing. Very little of it will take the form of 'sums'.

(*iii*) Make a calendar to display in the class. This can consist of a record of the weather, or of particularly exciting happenings each day, and the calendar can be filled in each day by a different child. It can be completed with drawings or with writing, or with simple diagrams such as weather symbols designed by the children themselves (Figure 3). The calendar can also be used for forward planning, and coming class events as well as regular fixtures can be written in on it. This encourages the children to develop the skills necessary to plan their lives and to organize their own activities.

(*iv*) Encourage the children, as individuals or in groups, to write – or draw – a diary. This helps them to structure and organize their memories and to distinguish the 'only just' past from the 'quite a long time ago' past.

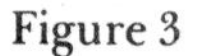


Figure 3

(*v*) Encourage the children to collect old photographs and artefacts, especially those which have personal associations. The greater the extent to which they can locate these in their past life the better, since this helps them to understand something of the passing of time.

(*vi*) Where possible, children can be asked to speculate about the future, both in terms of the immediate future (What am I going to do this weekend?), and the long-term future (What will cars look like in 2001?). They can design future houses, plan future cities and make future clothes. Equally, they can, at a younger age, write about what might happen over half-term, and speculate as to probable forthcoming events.

(*vii*) It is important to compare times and also ages. Television programme magazines are very useful in this context since children will frequently know which particular programme is on later than which other programme. Thus they can develop the concept of 'later than' and 'earlier than'. Children find it hard to estimate age in other people since they tend to judge on extraneous characteristics such as size: 'Fred must be older than Annie because he's bigger than her'! Candles on a birthday cake can help children grasp the concept of age since they are a mark of the passing of each year.

## Measuring time

When measuring time it is necessary to be aware of the difference between subjective and objective time. Subjective time is how time *feels* to us. Thus, if we are waiting at the bus-stop, five minutes can feel like a very long time especially if it's cold and we are late! However, when chatting to a friend, five minutes is no time at all. Objective time is the measurement of time by some means outside of ourselves such as a digital watch or a water-clock.

It is always a little difficult for children to grasp that we can, or *think* we can, measure time at all. In order to do so, we have to 'chop it up' into very small bits so that we can say: 'It is now six-forty-four and thirty seconds'. Children need to see and play with lots of examples of measuring time. Here are some suggestions:

(*i*) A candle clock. This consists of a candle which is reasonably slow to burn with a number of brightly coloured pins stuck vertically into its side. The candle is lit and, as the day progresses, the pins fall out and the children record what is happening at that time: 'The red pin fell out when we were just going out to play . . . the green pin fell out during story time . . .' This type of marking time is vividly concrete since the children can see – and smell – the passing of time.

(*ii*) Another very visual method of measuring the passing of time is with an egg or sand-timer. These can be very valuable in the classroom. They are easily and quickly set up several times during the day in order to persuade children to do some required activity – usually tidying up – quickly. The children rapidly become used to the amount of time allowed which is 3 minutes.

(*iii*) There are a number of other types of clock now available to schools: water clocks, sun dials, shadow clocks, pendulum clocks, etc. All of these are useful, particularly the sun dials and shadow clocks. Not only do these give a historical perspective to the topic, but they help children to perceive the passing of time as a natural phenomenon, like the sun rising and setting.

## Timing activities

Once children are becoming accustomed to the idea that we measure time, it is necessary for them to time themselves doing certain things and to see how many actions of a particular type they can do in a specified time. This helps them to develop a sense of time and to compare their own subjective notions of how long a thing takes with an objective measure.

(*i*) Time the children writing their own name or tying their shoelaces 20 times. Estimate first how long it will take. Remember to emphasize that this is not a race – some children have longer names than others. Encourage the children to time themselves building a model out of bricks. When they have finished, get them to estimate how long they have spent at the task and check this with the measured time. Time the children clearing up after the end of the day, or getting dressed after PE. This induces a sense of purpose and sometimes can help the children to perform these tasks more efficiently.

(*ii*) Give the children a set time – usually 1 or 3 minutes – in which to perform certain actions. How many times can you hop across the hall in 3 minutes? How many times can you tie a shoelace in 1 minute? This will develop a sense of how long 1 minute is, and of just how much one can, and can't, get done in that time.

(*iii*) Allow the children to test their subjective assessment of 1 minute by getting the whole class to shut their eyes and each child to raise their hand when they judge 1 minute to have passed. The children are allowed to open their eyes only when their hand has been raised. The percentage error on this activity is usually about 100%! This activity can be repeated at intervals during the term to see how fast the children improve.

(*iv*) Timing more long-term activities can be achieved by recording on a graph things like the growth of a bean. In this case the bean is planted (usually in wet blotting paper) and each day its growth is measured. At first it grows only from the root but after a day or so, it grows upwards as well. The growth of each part can be recorded on separate graphs or they can be aggregated on one graph as the total growth each day.

## Telling the time

The prevalence of digital watches has made the teaching of telling the time much more difficult. First, children can read off a digital display without having the faintest idea what time that means it is, or what is supposed to be happening at that time in the day. Secondly, digital watches mean that it is harder to approximate in telling the time because there is no immediately apparent visual relationship between the hour and the minutes passed.

(*i*) Children first of all need to become confident at recognizing the o'clocks, both on digital watches and on clockfaces.

(*ii*) Introduce the crucial notions of the halfway and the quarter marks – half past, quarter to, and quarter past. Make this neat little device for assisting children in this process. Cut two circles, the same size but different colours, out of sugar paper or card. Cut a radius in each of them. Interlock the two circles and turn one through another as shown (Figure 4). If the circle underneath is rotated a quarter of a circle at a time, then the *position* of the hands at a quarter past the hour, at half past and at a quarter to the hour is clearly demonstrated. To assist the effect, it is useful to draw a hand along the leading edge of the radius of the circle being rotated. This small gadget encourages children to tell the time by looking at the position of the hands rather than at the numbers that they point to. This will help them to tell the time by looking at the position of the hands, so it will not matter what type or quantity of figures are on the dial.

(*iii*) Once the children are able to recognize the halves and quarters, introduce words and phrases such as 'nearly' and 'just past'. Using these, the child can tell the time to an accuracy of 7½ minutes! At 8.40 they can say that, 'It's nearly a quarter to nine'. At this stage the children are still telling the time by looking at the position of the hands.

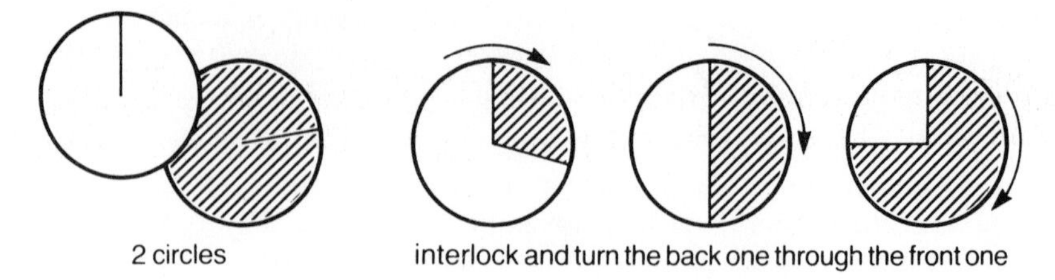


Figure 4

(*iv*) At a much later stage, once the children are really confident about their approximate time-telling, show them the function of the numbers around the edge with relation to the minute hand. Children need to be able to count in fives to be able to make use of this information. However, once they recognize that the numbers refer to sets of 5, most children can cope quite easily. It is a short step from this to 'to the minute' time-telling.

(*v*) Children usually have few problems *reading* the time on a digital watch. However, it is hard for them to get a sense of how far past one hour it is and how near the next. In order to understand this, they must have reached roughly the same stage as is required in order to recognize sets of five and the significance of the figures round the edge. They must appreciate that there are 60 minutes in a row and that half past must mean that 30 of them have gone. Once they are happy with fractions of 60, digital watches do not present much further trouble. It should be underlined that children should, by the time they are 11, be able to tell the time on both a digital display and a clockface.

(*vi*) Children are most likely to remember the names and order of the days in the week and the months in the year if these are associated with some events and happenings in their lives. So looking at calendars and diaries will be helpful, as will encouraging the children to give accounts of things that have happened to them and to talk about proposed and projected events.

(*vii*) An aid to remember the months is given by using the knuckles as shown (Figure 5). This helps children sort out the long months from the short ones.

(*viii*) Help the children to make themselves a 'time line'. This is a line on which are marked all the years from 15 years or so ago to the end of the century. The children fill in events that they can remember which have happened in their lifetimes, political or significant events which have happened in the past, and imagined events which will happen in the future.

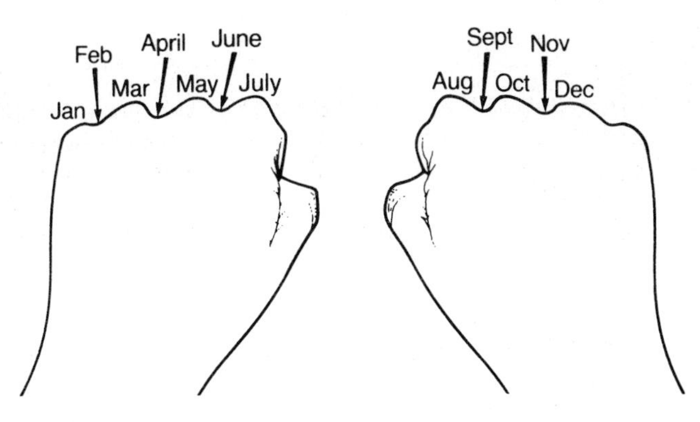


Figure 5

(*ix*) 'What will I be like in twenty years' time?' Ask the children to produce both a picture and a drawing under this heading. It is fascinating to see what they do and sometimes their expectations of themselves are not exactly what the teacher might be hoping for!

**Time calculations**

At the top end of the junior school, children can be encouraged to use time in various calculations. This means that they will be asked to use both their knowledge of what happens when, and their ability to calculate the number of minutes passed with reference to either a digital or analogue clock.

(*i*) Plan a journey using timetables (if possible use real ones). Ask questions about the best and most efficient routes. Allow the children to work out when the train arrives at each station on its route, how long it takes to get from one station to the next, and how long a person may be travelling to get from A to B.

(*ii*) Study the TV programme magazines and get the children to plan a week's television viewing. They may have to operate within various constraints: some time each evening for homework, no viewing after 9 o'clock on a weekday and a maximum number of hours TV at any one stretch or over the week. Setting tasks or problems of this kind produces a variety of learning strategies from the children. It is far more efficient as a means of helping them to work out such computations than textbook 'sums'. These activities have an immediate relevance that the child recognizes.

## Cost

Small children are aware of money and its purpose before they come to school. They know that one can buy things with money and that some things cost more than others. They have very probably handled some money although they will usually not be familiar with the different names of coins nor of their values.

### Coin recognition

If possible children need to handle real money in the school. This is because plastic or cardboard money, although it resembles real money in appearance, does not feel like it or weigh the same.

(*i*) Using real coins, do some coin rubbings by placing a piece of thin paper over a coin and crayoning gently over it with a wax crayon. These can look very nice mounted on matching coloured paper.

(*ii*) Make a series of money dominoes by mounting one real coin on a domino-shaped piece of card and writing an amount of money on the other half of the domino (Figure 6). Keep the amounts of money fairly simple – £1, 50p, 20p, 10p, 5p, 2p and possibly the 1p coins. Cover the cards with clear adhesive film in order to keep them strong. The children can then play with these dominoes either individually by laying them out in a long line in order, or in pairs or groups by playing a version of ordinary dominoes.

(*iii*) Allow the children to use coins in the classroom, for pretend shopping as well as for drawing around and general play. The more the children handle money themselves and talk about it, the better.

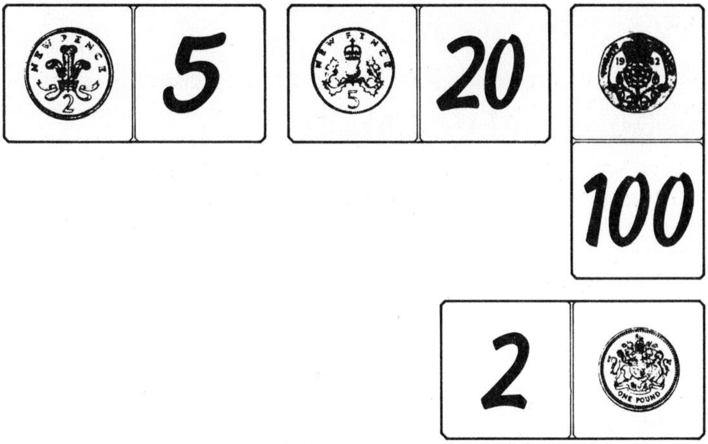

Figure 6

# 9

# Fractions and decimals

## Fractions

### Introducing fractions

The idea of simple fractions should be introduced as early in the infant school as possible. The use of the word 'half' is important since this can be used to mean 'one of two pieces' as in 'Give the guest the bigger half, Tommy', rather than to mean 'one of two *equal* pieces', which is its strictly mathematical meaning. Quite small children can be encouraged to divide things in halves, quarters and thirds. They notice the number of pieces that these divisions result in. Such work, all of it practical, paves the way for later, more formal fraction work. At this stage, absolutely no written recording is involved and the children are developing their ideas of halves and quarters, etc. and the use of appropriate language.

(*i*) Ask the children to find a half of the following things: the class; a banana; a handful of small bricks; a lump of plasticine; 50 pence; and any other things which come to hand. This is quite a difficult activity and so is suitable for junior children. It does involve them in thinking about such things as what happens if the class has an odd number of children in it, or whether to weigh the plasticine, or how to change the 50 pence.

(*ii*) Using Cuisenaire Rods, or Colour Factor, play around with halves, quarters and thirds. Which rods can be divided into thirds using other rods in the box? Can any rods be divided into halves, quarters and thirds? This can be followed up using numbers of bricks and seeing which numbers will divide equally into which fractions.

(*iii*) Fractions will arise out of many other contexts in the infant school and in the lower juniors. When the children are cooking, they might be asked to put in half a block of butter, or half a cup of milk. When some food or drink is being shared out they may be required

*Finding half of different things – string, plasticine, rice, etc.*

to have a quarter (of a bun) each. They will come to understand what 'half-term' is and also what 'half an hour' means. They realize what happens when half the class goes swimming or when a third of the school is absent. Children should be helped to recognize these fractions as they arise throughout their school experience.

**Fraction activities and investigations**

(*i*) Simple fraction jigsaws. Duplicate on squared paper a number of 4 by 4 squares. The idea is to divide these in half as many different ways as possible. It must be clear that they are to be divided into 2 equal pieces (Figure 1). Point out that mirror images could be described as the same, or different, shapes.

(*ii*) More complex fraction jigsaws. On squared paper, draw squares of 8 by 8 to start with. (The children may want to go on to larger squares later on.) They must then divide these squares into quarters, or at a later stage eighths or twelfths. The squares must be divided in such a way that no 2 quarters are the same shape. Once again, a decision must be made as to whether or not mirror images are going to be counted as the same shape. By using larger squares and more complicated fractions, this activity can prove very instruc-

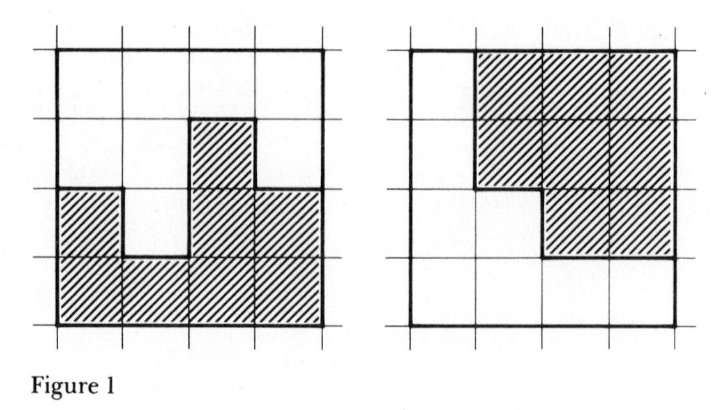

Figure 1

tive for children. The completed fraction squares make a lovely display. If two identical ones are drawn, one of them can be cut up so as to make a jigsaw (Figure 2).

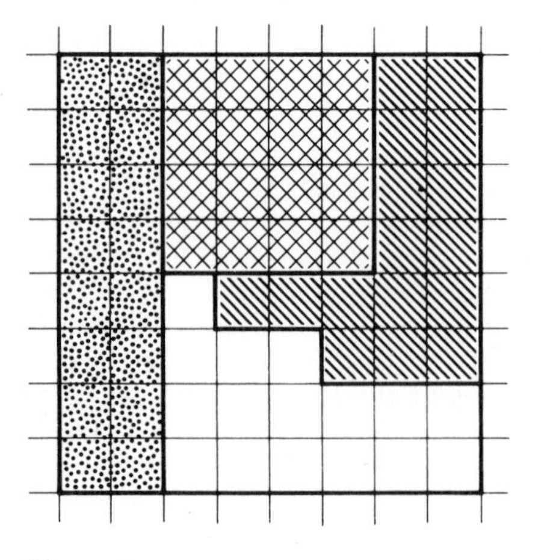

Figure 2

(*iii*) How many possible jigsaws? Using the activities outlined above, an investigation can be begun by asking how many possible ways there are of dividing a 4 by 4 square into halves without crossing any squares? What about a 5 by 5 square, a 6 by 6 square? How many ways are there of dividing an 8 by 8 square into quarters? Can one predict how many there would be for a 12 by 12 square? There are a number of different investigations possible here, depending upon the ages and abilities of the children.

*(iv)* Fraction walls. Building a fraction wall is an excellent aid to developing the idea of equivalent fractions. Using Cuisinaire Rods or Colour Factor, build a wall starting with the longest rod and build up as many rods as possible on top of it (Figure 3). Colour Factor is much better than Cuisinaire here since the longest rod is a 12. The same effect can be achieved by colouring a fraction wall on to squared paper. The children can write down the equivalent fractions as a means of recording their discoveries.

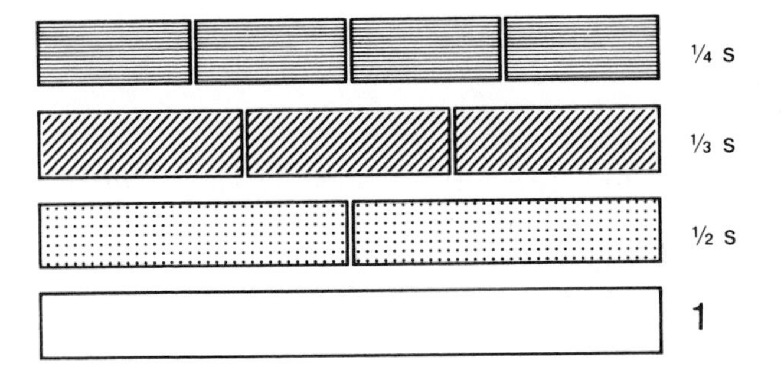


Figure 3

*(v)* Fraction graphs. Provided the children understand co-ordinates, they can make some very clear graphs of fractions which help sort out the equivalent fractions and demonstrate these as 'the same fraction'. Write down two equivalent fractions, for example, $\frac{1}{2}$ and $\frac{2}{4}$. Read the top part as the '*x*' co-ordinate and the bottom part as the '*y*' co-ordinate. Plot both points and join them with a line which continues to the edge of the graph. The line should pass through the origin (the point 0,0), and can act as a check. Then all the other points on this line will be equivalent fractions of $\frac{1}{2}$ (e.g. $\frac{3}{6}$, $\frac{4}{8}$ etc). Then another line can be drawn using another pair of equivalent fractions to give a different set of equivalent fractions (Figure 4).

*(vi)* Farey sequences. This investigation helps top juniors to explore some of the properties of fractions. Farey sequences of fractions are sequences which start with a fraction of the form $\frac{1}{x}$ and continue with all the fractions above that arranged in order up to $\frac{x}{x}$ or 1. Equivalent fractions are not included. Investigate Farey sequences of order 4 and above (e.g. $\frac{1}{5}$, $\frac{1}{4}$, $\frac{1}{3}$, $\frac{2}{5}$, $\frac{1}{2}$, $\frac{3}{5}$, $\frac{2}{3}$, $\frac{3}{4}$, $\frac{4}{5}$, 1). Look carefully at each Farey sequence. What does the order of the sequence depend on? How many fractions are there in each one? Does this depend on the order? Are there any patterns to the numerators of the 4?

(*vii*) Half rectangles. Investigate dividing different rectangles in half. Is there any pattern to the number of ways a 2 by 4 rectangle can be divided, or a 2 by 5 rectangle, a 2 by 6 rectangle, etc? How do the children know that they have found all the ways?

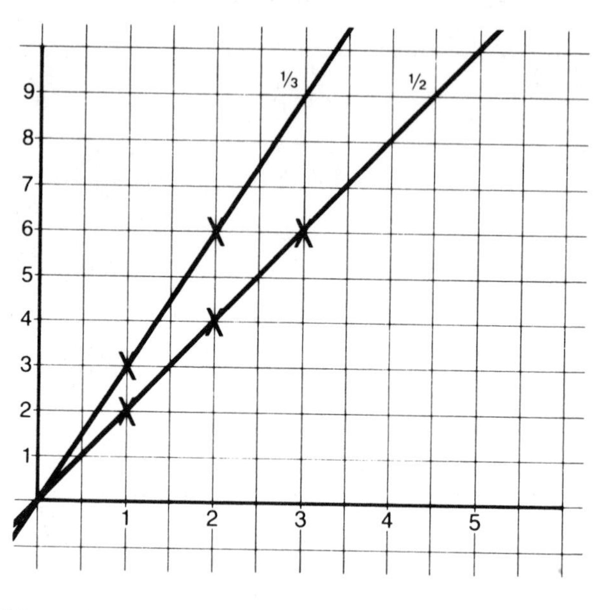


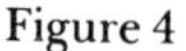
Figure 4

(*viii*) Fold in half. Try folding a rectangular piece of paper in half in at least five different ways. Which ways are estimates? Which ways are accurate? This investigation sounds simple but it illuminates very effectively how much the children understand about halves, estimates, and how well they can think in terms of spatial awareness.

## Decimals

The easiest way to introduce decimals is through practical work with measures (using the metric system) and money.

### Some ideas for decimal activities

(*i*) Laying down the money. Using real or imitation coins and a base board for decimals (Figure 5), name a sum of money between £1 and £5. The children lay out this sum on the base board. The sums of money should be read out loud and can sometimes be given in pence and sometimes as fractions of a pound. The children can also be asked to write down the sum of money named (Figure 5).

| £1 | 10p | 1p |
|---|---|---|
| £1 | 3 | 5 |

Figure 5

(*ii*) Abacus. Using a decimal abacus the children can formalize what they were doing when they were laying out the sums of money. A sum of money is named and the children place the appropriate rings on the abacus to represent the sum. The abacus can also be used to assist children with money computations. But even when adding sums like £3.65 and £2.78, children can estimate the answer first and thus keep developing a feel for the 'size' of decimals. In fact, in adult life, it is often more important to have a rough idea of what the answer is going to be than it is to be able to work out the answer exactly. For example, if a person is going shopping and they want to know whether to take a £5 note or a £10 note with them to cover all expenses, it is more useful to be able to do a quick estimate of the proposed purchases than a long and accurate paper and pencil calculation.

(*iii*) Change. Children can also give change using the abacus. Special money abacuses exist for exactly this purpose but an ordinary decimal abacus will do. Choose an amount to spend, say £2.58, and represent this amount on the abacus. Now decide what note to 'pay' with, for example, £5. Count on up by adding to the abacus until £5 is reached. This is a version of 'gazuptas' or shop keepers' addition mentioned in earlier chapters.

(*iv*) Decimal squares. Draw and duplicate enough 10 by 10 cm squares for the children to have at least two each. Each child, using only one colour, draws a pattern on their first square. They then count the number of squares they have coloured. On their second square they colour an identical number of squares but this time they colour them in rows (Figure 6).

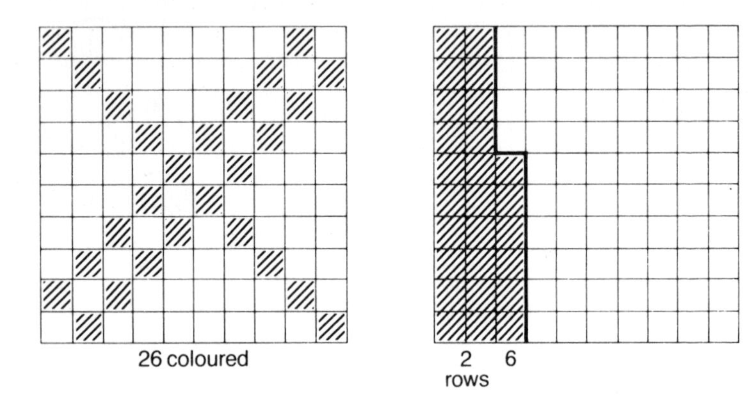


Figure 6

The child can then express the number of squares coloured as a decimal of the square. There are 100 possible squares to colour, so the child that has coloured 39 of them in their pattern has coloured .39 of the large square. This is a very visual and attractive method of demonstrating decimals. The finished patterns make an attractive display and it sometimes proves very difficult to estimate from the original pattern what decimal of the square has been coloured until the square containing the coloured rows is seen. This is usually a very popular activity with children.

(*v*) Decimal pontoon. Make a pack of about 50 cards each with one number between 0 and 1 written on it, for example, 0.6, 0.75, 0.43, etc. Cover the cards with adhesive film to make them durable. They are then shuffled into a pack and placed in the middle of the table. One card is given to each player. The player has then to place a bet as to their likelihood of getting as near as possible to, but not over, 1, when a second card is added. A second card is then dealt to each player. Those who are now in the position of being 'bust', that is, of having more than 1, must retire from this hand. The others can either 'buy' another card by laying down a further bet, or they can 'stick'. If they stick they wait until the other players have finished drawing cards. Up to 5 cards may be drawn. The player who is nearest to 1 is the winner. Any player who has 5 cards totalling under 1, beats anyone except a player who scores exactly 1. This game can also be played with a pack of cards where the decimals are sums of money (£0.67, £0.39, etc.) instead of just numbers. In that case, the target number is £1. Children enjoy this game very much and it is most effective in developing their grasp of decimals under 1.

(*vi*) Encourage children to convert into decimals by giving them calculations involving measures given in a mixture of units, which they can do using a calculator. Suppose they have to work out the total length of a room which is made up of the following: a bookshelf unit, 11.4 dm long; a length of wall, 3.7 m long; a small window, 75 cm wide, and a length of exhibition board, 168 cm across. The total length must be given in metres. This allows the child to decide in what unit to perform the calculation and to work out all the other units in terms of that unit, and then to convert into metres if necessary at the end.

## Decimals as fractions

Modern educational thinking in mathematics emphasizes the base work aspect of the decimal system (seeing and presenting decimals as a part of the base 10 system which the children have been coming to understand through their work on place value). This work is facilitated through the use of structural apparatus such as Dienes blocks, base boards and abacuses. The fractional aspect of decimals should therefore be left until children are thoroughly familiar with how the system works.

(*i*) Demonstrate to top juniors the connections between fractions and decimals by getting them to use a calculator to divide the numerator (the top part of the fraction) by the denominator. Thus 1 divided by 2 is 0.5, $\frac{3}{8}$ is 0.375, etc. Which fractions turn into recurring decimals and why? What happens if we multiply $\frac{1}{3}$ by 3? What happens if we multiply 0.33 by 3? How can they both be correct? It is useful for top juniors to consider these relationships because they form connections with the work they will be doing in secondary mathematics.

(*ii*) Try out some fraction/decimal investigations with top juniors. $\frac{50}{100}$ is 0.5. What is $\frac{51}{100}$? Is it more or less than 0.5? Add 1 to the top and the bottom of any fraction, and see if the effect is always the same. What happens if 1 is subtracted from the top and the bottom of any fraction? Is $^{49}/_{99}$ more or less than 0.5?

(*iii*) Third-year and fourth-year juniors can use their calculators to work out the sums when they are only given the answers. Thus, if they are told that the volume of a cube is 53 cm, they can try to work out the side in centimetres. If the area of an oblong playground is 1624 m, what could the lengths of its sides be? Is there more than one possible answer to this? The process of calculating square roots and cube roots and associated sums by trial and error develops the children's skills of estimation and judgement. They need an approximate answer in order to get going. Thus, such tasks are also good for their multiplication tables!

(*iv*) A further exploration of the relationship between decimals and fractions can be encouraged by asking the children to convert $^1/_7$, $^2/_7$ . . . $^6/_7$ into decimals. What is noticed? Repeat this with fractions of denominator 13.

## Calculations involving decimals and fractions

As discussed in chapters 5 and 6, the prevalence of calculators both in school, in the home, and at work means that paper and pencil calculations are no longer essential in the way that they were. It is therefore not usually considered necessary nowadays to teach the long multiplication of decimals, or addition or subtraction of mixed denominator fractions.

(*i*) Fraction calculations. Children should be asked to perform calculations which involve working out a given fraction of a number, or adding or subtracting fractions with the same denominator. Examples of such calculations include:

- $^1/_5$ of the class has gone swimming, $^1/_3$ is doing music, $^1/_6$ is absent. If the class consists of 30 children, how many children are still in the classroom?
- If $^1/_{10}$, $^3/_{10}$ and $^4/_{10}$ of the class are respectively using 1 of 3 different mathematics books, what fraction of the class do they represent in all?

(*ii*) Equivalent fractions. Children should be capable of adding equivalent fractions and of converting fractions to a common denominator. The easier way to convert one fraction into another is by using the multiplication square. Reading any one row as the top half of the fractions and any other lower row as the bottom half of the fractions will automatically give the set of equivalent fractions

(Figure 7).

$\frac{1}{3} = \frac{2}{6} = \frac{3}{9}$ etc.

| 1 | 2 | 3 | 4 | 5 | 6 | 7 | 8 | 9 | 10 |
|---|---|---|---|---|---|---|---|---|---|
| 2 | 4 | 6 | 8 | 10 | 12 | 14 | 16 | 18 | 20 |
| 3 | 6 | 9 | 12 | 15 | 18 | 21 | 24 | 27 | 30 |
| 4 | 8 | 12 | 16 | 20 | 24 | 28 | 32 | 36 | 40 |
| 5 | 10 | 15 | 20 | 25 | 30 | 35 | 40 | 45 | 50 |
| 6 | 12 | 18 | 24 | 30 | 36 | 42 | 48 | 54 | 60 |
| 7 | 14 | 21 | 28 | 35 | 42 | 49 | 56 | 63 | 70 |
| 8 | 16 | 24 | 32 | 40 | 48 | 56 | 64 | 72 | 80 |
| 9 | 18 | 27 | 36 | 45 | 54 | 63 | 72 | 81 | 90 |
| 10 | 20 | 30 | 40 | 50 | 60 | 70 | 80 | 90 | 100 |

$\frac{1}{4} = \frac{2}{8} = \frac{3}{12}$ etc.

Figure 7

(*iii*) Decimal calculations. Children can be required to add and subtract decimals and to understand the principles of multiplying and dividing decimal fractions so that they can estimate a reasonable answer and check it using a calculator. They can learn to add and subtract decimals using the same equipment that they used when they were learning how to add 2- and 3-figure numbers – base boards, structural apparatus, and abacuses. Once again, they should always be encouraged to estimate first so that they develop good judgement as to the order of magnitude of the answer.

Children's understanding of the principles of multiplying and dividing decimals may best be developed through multiplying fractions. They must have a sound comprehension of multiplying as 'sets of', so that, for example, $\frac{1}{2} \times \frac{1}{2}$ is seen as ½ *of* ½ and therefore as ¼. The idea that, when fractions are multiplied, the answer is smaller than the original numbers is counter-intuitive and children need practice and experience to understand it. They need to take ½ an orange and then to take ½ of that ½ in order to see the result as sensible.

Fractions and decimals arise commonly out of contexts other than mathematics lessons. The more children are encouraged to deal with these concepts in these other contexts, the better their understanding of them is likely to be. The more familiar decimals and fractions become, and the more practice the children get at adding, subtracting, multiplying and dividing them in context, the more their comprehension and general 'familiarity' with these ideas is increased and consolidated.

# 10

# Early shape and basic topology

## Early shape

When children come to school they have already encountered an almost infinite number of shapes, some of which they can name. However, much of the language used in everyday life to describe shapes is not as precise as it must be in mathematics. From an early age children recognize phrases like: 'Bring me the round one . . .'; 'Try the other side . . .'; 'Mind the corners . . .'; 'Find the square box . . .'. There are lots of questions a mathematician might ask about some of the words used here, such as: Does 'round' refer to a circle (2 dimensions), or a sphere (3 dimensions)? Does 'side' mean edge or face? Is a square box a cube or a cuboid? In practice, of course, the context of such questions, and the gestures which may accompany them, will preclude ambiguity.

### Sorting shapes

Children can be encouraged to sort shapes from the reception class onwards. But they should not sort only regular shapes, or only 2-dimensional shapes. Also, the categories into which they sort should depend upon the purpose behind the sorting and must not consist only of named shapes (e.g. circle, square, oblong, etc.). It is not as important that children can *name* shapes in this way as that they recognize the *properties* of certain shapes.

(*i*) Sorting boxes, cartons, rolls, etc. to make junk models. Which ones will roll? Which ones have corners and how many? Which ones glue best to each other? This type of question concentrates the children's attention on the properties of these shapes in relation to the task in hand – namely making a junk model. The children may also come to recognize certain properties as ones which two or more shapes have in common. Perhaps several boxes will have a square cross-section (Figure 1).

After sorting their materials the children can be asked to build

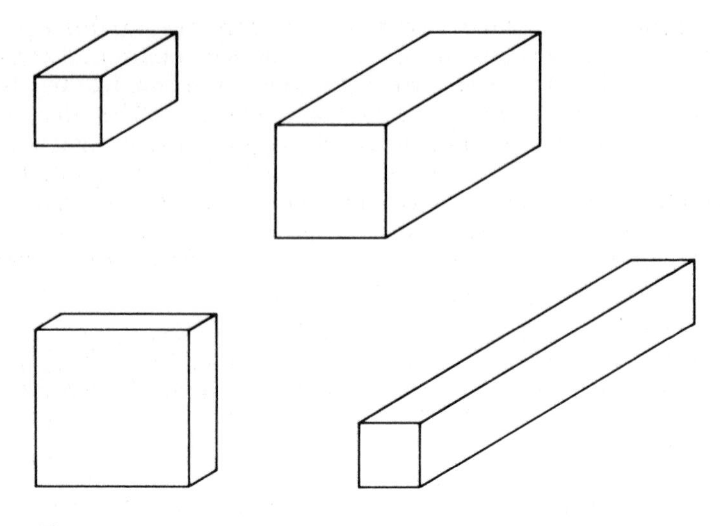

Figure 1

models which conform to certain criteria. So, they might be required to build the tallest tower possible using only 6 objects. This will entail a lot of further sorting and selection – some boxes will be short and fat one way round and long if they are turned on edge. Curved surfaces do not glue well together and therefore do not make for a stable structure. Setting a task like this: *Build a model using only 6 objects that is as low as possible, but only 1 box may rest on the ground*, means that the parameters of the task itself impose a rationale for sorting and a strategy for building. This encourages children to use the properties of the various shapes and enables them not only to notice these properties but also to become more familiar with them.

(*ii*) Using Logiblocks. Logiblocks – as their name suggests – are used for activities intended to develop logical thinking and set-theoretic concepts (see chapter 2). However, this does not exclude the possibility of using them for activities to develop ideas concerning the properties of various shapes. The Logiblocks can be sorted according to all sorts of criteria: Which have straight edges and which do not? Which have corners and how many? Which are fat and which are thin? Which are the same when turned round through one right angle? Logiblocks can also be used to help the children develop an understanding of conservation of shape. This is the idea that the shape of an object does not alter when the object changes position. A square is still a square when it is turned on to one corner, a triangle remains a triangle when it is standing on its point. Sometimes the development of this idea can be assisted by holding up a Logiblock and asking children to shut their eyes and then open them after a few seconds and say if it has been turned round at all. After the shape has been turned through, for example, 90°, the children are again asked to name it. Some children will be reluctant to call it the same name, whilst others will be quite certain that it must be the same since it is still the same Logiblock. This activity also has implications for symmetry development. Some shapes can be rotated through 90° and when the children open their eyes, they cannot tell if it has been moved at all (e.g. a square). With other shapes, this is not so (e.g. an oblong).

(*iii*) Tesselating shapes. Children can come to distinguish those shapes which tesselate from those which do not. At first they will want to try out as wide a variety of shapes as possible. They need to experiment to discover which shapes will tesselate and they must do this with irregular as well as regular shapes. It is interesting that 'regular' is one of the words that tends to be used to mean something different in ordinary usage from its strict mathematical sense. A regular shape is, strictly speaking, one which has equal length sides. This definition includes a square but excludes an oblong. Does it include a circle? It is also important to remember that a rectangle is any shape with four right-angles and that squares are therefore rectangles, as are oblongs. An oblong is a rectangle which is *not* a square.

(*iv*) Children can also sort all kinds of different shapes, some that they have cut out and made themselves and some that have been made for them. These should include shapes with curved edges, and shapes with only straight edges, shapes with no symmetry at all and others which are symmetrical. The children can sort the shapes in many different ways according to various criteria (these have some curly edges and some straight, these have all straight edges . . .). They can classify them and describe them to each other (that one looks like a house, that one looks like a boat . . . etc.). The more the children are encouraged to play with shapes, to create their own, and to describe them, the more they become familiar with the properties of the various shapes and of the relationships between them.

## Activities involving shape

Playing with, learning about and using shapes are sometimes underrated activities in primary schools. Some children develop spatial awareness by playing with construction toys and the like outside school. However some children, who may be advanced at computation and perfectly competent in other areas of mathematics, do not develop spatial awareness. At first, this might not be thought to matter very much, and indeed, such children can often continue right through the primary school without anyone becoming concerned at all. However, the further such children continue in mathematics, the more this omission comes to matter. As they progress in the subject an ability to think in three dimensions (at least!), and to visualize patterns and symmetries, becomes more and more necessary. There are also all the related disciplines, such as engineering, craft, design and technology, which rely even more heavily upon good spatial awareness. It can often turn out to be the girls who lose out if this awareness is not developed at primary level since many of the toys which best assist its development are marketed towards boys.

(*i*) Construction toys. All the children should be encouraged to build models using one of the many construction toys available for this purpose. Children can make their own models and can then both write about them and draw them. Sometimes it helps to set a task within quite narrow and well-defined parameters, especially if the child has little or no experience of constructing. Just to be told to build a model can be very daunting, especially if there are much more competent and experienced children around who need no persuasion. So a child might be asked to make a house three storeys high, or a robot-cat or a marble-run, depending upon the construction set to be used. Children who are timid about building things need time to play with the materials first so that they come to feel more familiar with how they work, and only then they will be able to think about designing their own models. Once children can, with some confidence, build their own models, they can draw them. Once again, this can be made quite a demanding task by restricting *how* they draw their models – from the top looking down bird's-eye view, for example.

(*ii*) Lego. This is now such an important apparatus in schools and one which is used in so many subjects, that it is worth a section of its own. With the development of more and more control technology the use of Lego in schools is likely to increase rather than the reverse. Once again, children will vary a great deal in their expertise with this material. Some will play with it all day, if given the chance, and some never seem to look at it. It is these latter who need to be encouraged. Lego is not just important for the development of spatial awareness. Children should become familiar with the materials themselves since technical Lego, with its complicated systems of gears and different methods of driving motored structures, is becoming more and more a part of craft, design and technology as well as the new and rapidly expanding area of control technology.

(*iii*) Multilink. This apparatus is so simple to fit together that it can be used with the smallest children in the school. Set a task such as 'make a robot' and watch how different children approach it. Once the children have made their robot they can play with it. After a bit, they will not only have designed a robot but a character for it as well! They can then draw and name their robot. (It is interesting to note that children's robots are, in my experience, nearly always masculine!) With older children this activity can be further developed by requiring that the robot is symmetrical or that it should be drawn to scale.

(*iv*) Using 2-dimensional shapes, children can be asked to create a class or group picture. They will require a mixture of regular and irregular shapes cut out of either paper or fabric. Doing this activity together provides an excellent opportunity for the children to discuss the shapes that they are using and the language they use often generates as much learning as the actual handling of the shapes and trying to fit them together to make the objects desired for the picture. Ideas which work well in this context include an undersea-view, a space picture, and a city-scape. It seems to work best if the children create their own object for the picture by mounting it on their own piece of paper and then cutting around it and sticking it on to the class picture in the appropriate place (photo). This way they are not all crowding around the final picture and mistakes can be rectified in time.

(*v*) Draw a large recognizable shape in the middle of the page – a square, a triangle or an oblong. Cut round it. Now cut similar shapes from all round the inside of the perimeter. Place the original shape on a piece of paper in a contrasting colour (black and white paper works especially well in this activity) and arrange each of the smaller cut-out shapes alongside the hole from which it was cut. This can make a stunning design and children may want to do two or three to experiment with the different effects which it is possible to achieve (Figure 2). Put together, these can make a most attractive display.

(*iv*) Tangrams. Children of all ages enjoy playing with tangrams and making different patterns by arranging the pieces. The usual tangram is shown here (Figure 3), but there are a number of variations on this theme. When using tangrams with infants, cut out the pieces in strong card so that they have something to use as a template. Then they can draw round these on gummed paper squares and arrange the pieces prior to sticking them down.

(*vii*) Drawing unseen shapes. This is very definitely a junior

*Making pictures of different shapes*

activity. Erect a barrier between two children so that neither can see what the other is drawing. Each child then draws a shape or very basic picture. By questioning each other, each child must reproduce the other's picture. This process may involve such questions as:

How many closed shapes does your picture contain?
How many squares, oblongs, circles, etc?
Is this shape above that one?
Is this shape inside that one?
Are the two lines vertical?
Are they parallel?

This activity is much harder than it at first appears. But it is a very worthwhile one, since the mathematical language which emerges is usually so rewarding. The children have to be as specific as they can, and much of their terminology and description, which can be rather 'woolly' and imprecise, becomes much tighter and more refined. The activity is an unusual one in the study of shape in that it requires a lot of language rather than visual perception or art or construction skills and also it is an activity which involves topological notions as well as geometric ones.

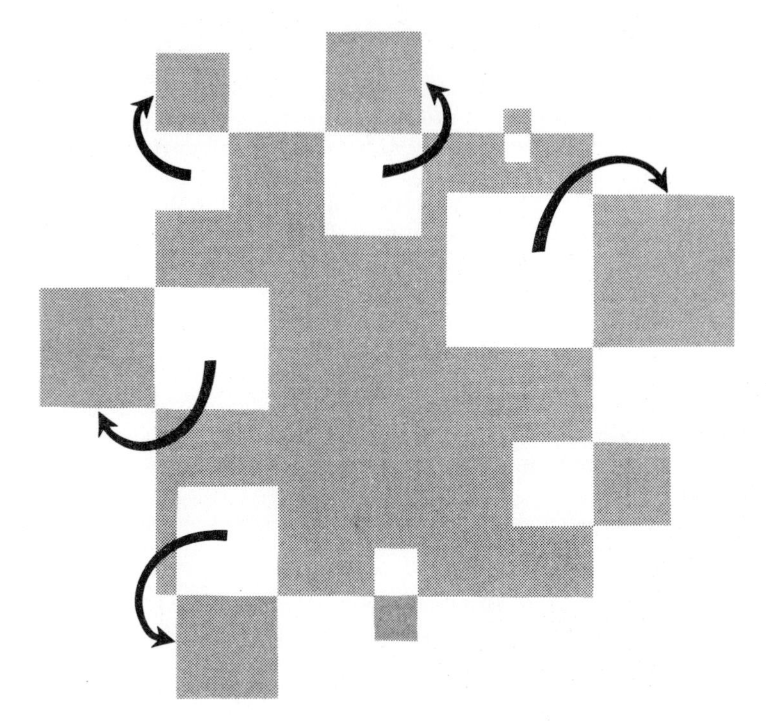

Figure 2

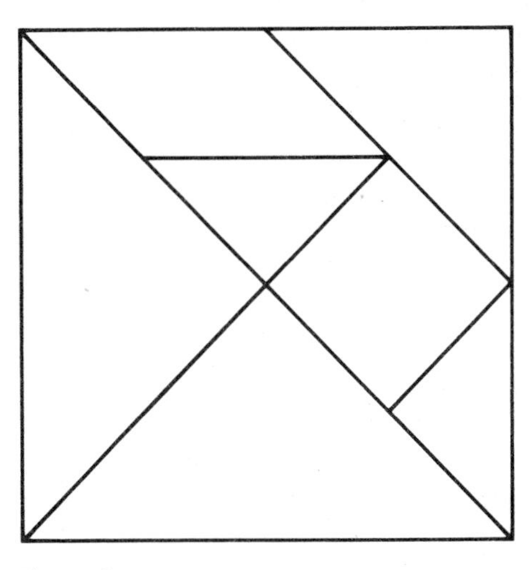

Figure 3

## Early topology

Topology is very hard to define. It is sometimes referred to as 'rubber sheet geometry'. Where geometry is concerned with measurement, with size and angle, topology is concerned with the relationships between shapes and space. Thus the measurements of a shape are of no interest in topology, but the fact that a shape has a hole in it so that it looks like a doughnut will be relevant.

From the nursery upwards children are employing topological notions of space and shape. There are those who argue that children view the world topologically rather than geometrically and that some of the ideas of Euclidean geometry have to be imposed on to a basically topological structure in terms of how children interpret reality. However, it is certainly the case that children do understand some of the basic concepts in this area when they come to school and that it is important to build on their existing knowledge.

### Closed and open shapes

The idea that we can make a distinction between those shapes which are closed and those which are open (Figure 4) can be introduced to infants with reference to fields and open gates.

The children are asked to draw or build a number of 'safe' fields in which to keep a precious animal. They may then be asked to sort a series of diagrams on cards to see if they are open or closed. It may help to colour the drawings to find out if they are really open or closed shapes.

### Topological relationships

Topology involves thinking about the relationship between one 'space' and another. Thus if a shape is closed it divides reality into two 'spaces', and it is possible for me to be 'inside' or 'outside'. The relationship of junctions to lines enclosing spaces is also topological. Also relevant is the idea that some patterns can be drawn without lifting the pen from the page. Small children are usually well aware of the difference between inside and outside, and also of the relationship of one junction to another. The more that the children are thinking in terms of a process, rather than a product, with regard to shape, the more they are likely to be thinking topologically.

Figure 4

**Routes**

If children are encouraged to describe their routes to and from a place – the way to the library, how to get to the toilet, where the Head teacher's office is – the more they will develop the idea that we can best describe such routes using topological notions rather than measurements. Thus I may describe a route: 'You go *into* a room and then *out* of the door and along the corridor. Then you come to a place where another corridor meets the one you're walking along. You turn along this one and you go to the end where you come *outside* into the playground . . .' This explanation of how to find somewhere does not rely on measurements of any kind. It is all about process, being concerned with the actual *how* in how to get there, whereas the more traditional geometric explanation of the same route might involve the following: 'Enter a room which is about 80 metres long. At right angles to the way I was facing when I came in is a corridor leading off the room. This seems to be about 100 metres long and halfway down it on the left there is another corridor at right angles . . .' Since children do already have quite a lot of ideas about the processes of getting from A to B, we can draw on them and concentrate on building up their feel for what relationship one isolatable piece of space has with another, and which pieces of space are isolable.

## Junctions

Even quite small children can be encouraged to develop the idea of a junction as a place where two or more routes meet. They can draw maps of routes and mark out the junctions. They can draw squiggly patterns and count the number of closed spaces and junctions. These can then be coloured (Figure 5).

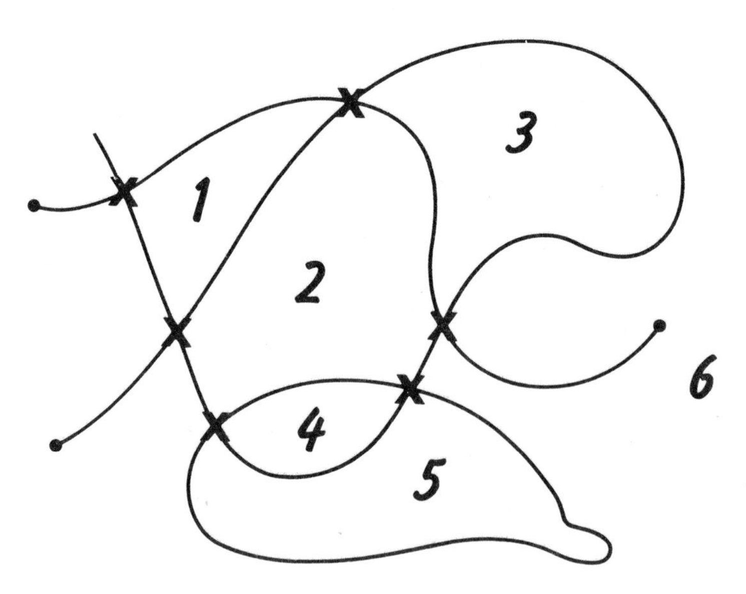


Figure 5

## The four colour problem

No pattern or design has yet been discovered which needs more than four colours to colour it so that no two adjacent spaces are the same colour. The children can be told this and also told that they will make mathematical history if they can find a pattern or map that needs five colours. The four colour theorem has not yet been proved mathematically, so it is theoretically possible that there exists a map which needs five colours or more to colour it.

Since topology is about the relationships between space and junctions, some of the ideas that children already have about the giving of directions and the drawing and designing of patterns, all of which have nothing to do with measurements, can be used as the starting point for this topic.

# 11

# Shape and more topology

In the junior school the topic of shape too often involves formulae rather than practical work. The junk modelling and construction done in infant school is abandoned for static diagrams and pictures on a page. Juniors, as well as infants, need practical activities to help them develop their ideas. Without a firm base of practical experience children can fail to acquire some of the concepts and ideas which enable them to proceed satisfactorily to further mathemetics in the secondary school and beyond.

## Shape

In the junior school it is as necessary to consider the properties of various shapes as it was in the infant school. By the time they leave primary school, children should have a thorough grasp of the names and properties of the more common shapes and their classification. They should be able to calculate the areas and volumes of common 2-dimensional and 3-dimensional shapes, and they should be able to draw simple shapes accurately and to scale if required.

### Accurate drawing

To start with, children need to be shown how to use a ruler in order to measure a line accurately. They should then practise using a ruler to draw lines of a given length. Once they can do this, it is less boring for them if this skill is practised in context as it arises out of other work. Possible activities include:

(*i*) Creating straight line patterns. A ruler can be used to draw a circle – or least the envelope of a circle – by the following method. Put a dot in the middle of the page. Place one edge of the ruler up against the dot and move the ruler slowly clockwise, drawing a line along the opposite edge to the dot every time it is moved (Figure 1). This technique can be used to produce figures of eight as well and

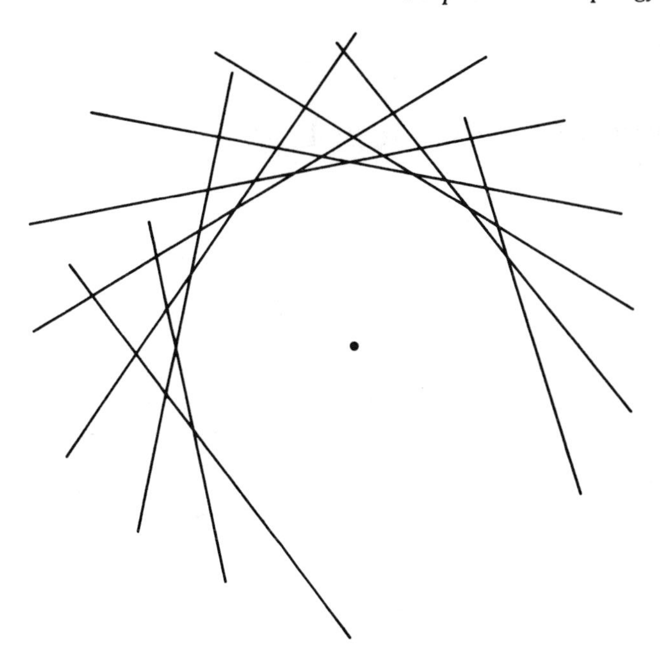

Figure 1

the resulting patterns can make a very attractive display.

A completely different way of making straight line patterns is to cover a piece of paper with a large number of haphazardly placed straight lines, that the whole paper is criss-crossed. The child then colours a carefully made selection of the spaces between the lines so as to obtain a pattern, or initials, or a picture. This can be an attractive element in a display.

A further idea for a straight line pattern is the 'mystic rose'. This is created by marking points around the edge of a circle and joining every point marked to every other point marked. The lines thus crossing the circle form a 'mystic rose' in the centre of the circle (Figure 2). The more points there are, the more satisfactory the final product.

(*ii*) Drawing a scale plan. Children can be asked to draw a plan of a room or set of buildings. This is quite a difficult task for lower juniors. They have to be able to 'see' the room in their mind's eye and to convey that image to paper. But the abstraction involved makes it a very useful activity for developing their spatial awareness. When the children come to draw their plan neatly, it will involve them in quite a lot of measuring, and drawing lines of given lengths to some

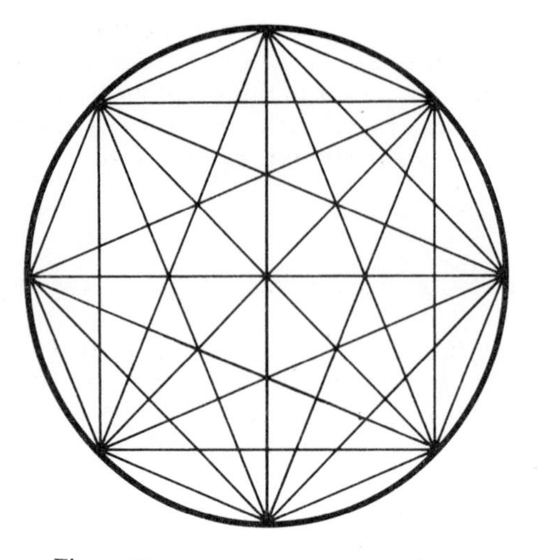

Figure 2

considerable degree of accuracy. It is interesting for children to look at the plans which architects draw up so that they can see the sorts of conventions which are employed as regards signs for doors, windows, etc.

(*iii*) Drawing a circle. In the infant school, circles will be drawn by drawing round a suitable object or template. However, when the children get to junior school, they can develop the technique of drawing circles using the idea that a circle consists of a point moving around another fixed point at a constant distance. At first this will involve drawing a circle using a piece of string or thread fixed in the middle of the page with a pin and with a loop for the pencil point at its loose end. After trying this, children will fully understand the principles involved and can move on to using one of the many types of compass now available for this age range. Learning how to draw curved lines with accuracy is very useful, and it can also produce some very pretty patterns for display.

(*iv*) Designing a 3-dimensional structure. If children are asked to design, and then build, a particular structure (e.g. a bridge), the design work can fall into two stages. First, they will sketch out a rough plan which will form the basis of the design. Then they will need to draw out the complete design accurately, and probably to scale. Finally they will build a proto-type. There is an immense amount of mathematics involved in such a project: estimation and judgement; addition and subtraction; scale work; measurement; etc. Because the mathematics is all in context and arises naturally as a part of the task set, and it is necessary to do it in order to solve the problem, many children will work quite hard at it although, were the same requirements to be made of them out of context, they probably would not do so. This echoes the Curriculum Document No. 3 which emphasizes that all skills should, where possible, be taught and practised in context.

## Construction of more complex shapes, and further activities

As the children get older they need to experiment by constructing more complex 3-dimensional models and by approaching the making and classifying of 2-dimensional shapes in a more rigorous, structured and precise manner. The importance of practical activities does not diminish as the children get older. Rather, it becomes increasingly important that the concepts are acquired and that the children do not simply learn by rote a set of semi-meaningless formulae which have no more reality than that of a static diagram on the page. Activities which involve these sort of practical experiences include:

(*i*) Finding the areas of different shapes. The children will be familiar with finding the area of a 2-dimensional shape by counting unit squares. They will also realize that it is possible to shorten this process in the case of a rectangle by counting the number of rows and the number of columns, and multiplying the two. With this knowledge, it is easy to extend their understanding to include the means of finding the area of a triangle, a circle and almost any combination of these shapes.
Area of a triangle: Draw a triangle on squared paper. Draw a rectangle round it which has the same base and height (Figure 3). Find the area of the rectangle. Cut out the rectangle carefully. Then

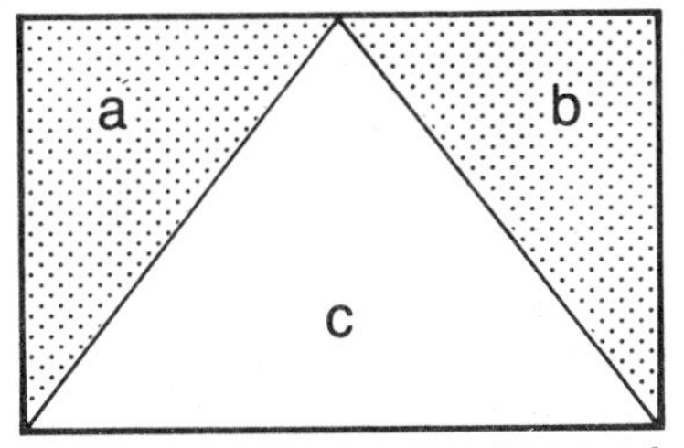


a and b are cut out and placed on top of c

Figure 3

cut the triangle from the rectangle, and the two smaller triangles in the 'bit left over'. If these two smaller triangles are now laid adjacently on top of the triangle from the middle they will be seen to cover it exactly. Thus the original triangle occupies exactly half the space of the rectangle. This can be shown very simply using the special case of a right-angled triangle. Thus it can be demonstrated that the area of a triangle is always half that of a rectangle, namely, half the base multiplied by the height.

Area of a circle: The children can count the number of squares that a circle covers, approximating by counting up the half squares (Figure 4). The area can be demonstrated to be always three times the radius squared (approximately). The ratio of the diameter to the circumference or Pi can be introduced as follows: take several pieces of string and cut each one the length of the circumference of a circular object of known diameter; stick the pieces of string on to a graph where the $x$-axis represents the diameter of the object, and the $y$-axis represents the length of the pieces of string or the circumference (Figure 5).

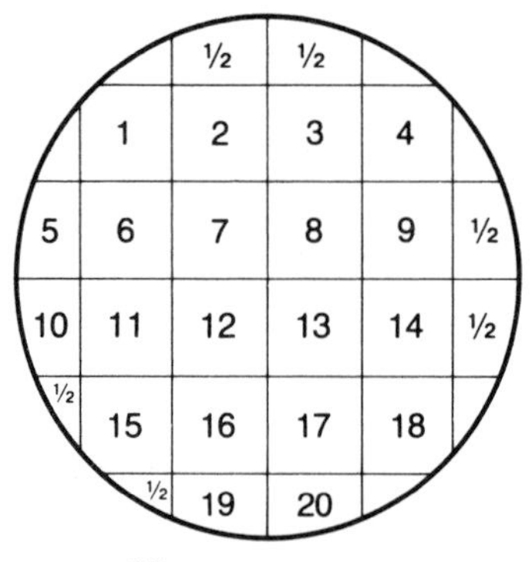


Figure 4

The slope or gradient of the straight line graph thus formed should be approximately 3 or $\pi$. In other words, in each case the circumference is about three times the diameter. Once this ratio has been established as about 3, the area of the circle can be expressed in terms of Pi, as $\pi r^2$. The children will need a lot of practice trying this out and demonstrating that it works by drawing circles on squared paper and counting the squares and then checking the area using $\pi r^2$.

Areas of other shapes: Providing a shape can be divided up into shapes for which the area can be calculated (Figure 6), it is easy to

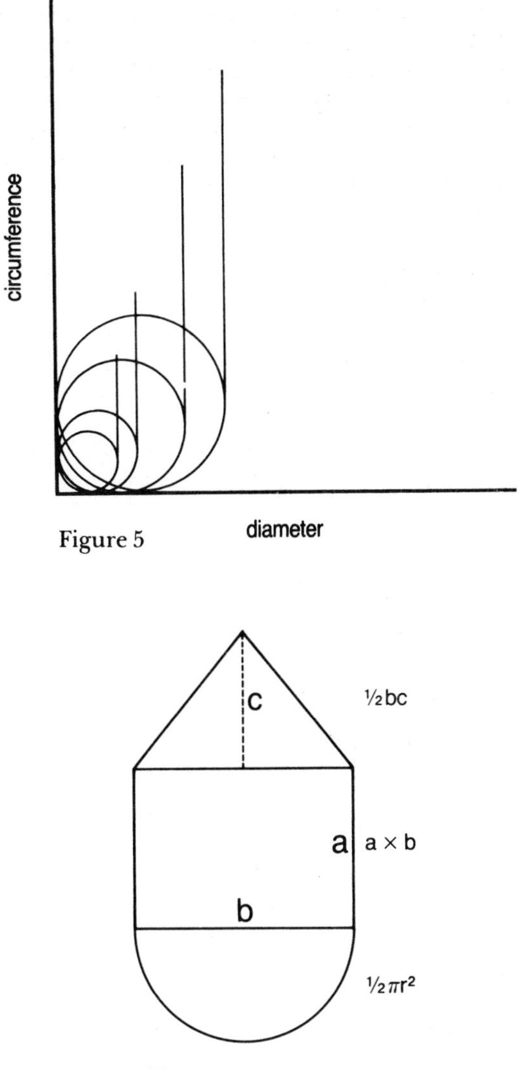


Figure 5

Figure 6

find the area by adding together that of all the various pieces. Otherwise, the shape must be drawn out on squared paper and the unit squares counted up.

(*ii*) Quadrilaterals. There is frequently some confusion about quadrilaterals. Sometimes, children seem to think of rectangles and squares as disjoint sets. On other occasions, a square which is turned on to one corner is called a diamond! Children can experiment with making different types of quadrilaterals by playing around with a peg-board. They can try to find as many different ones as possible. Then, having found what they consider to be all of them, the children can be asked to draw them and to explain the logic employed to find them and what criteria could be used sorting them. A large Venn diagram can be used to sort these (Figure 7).

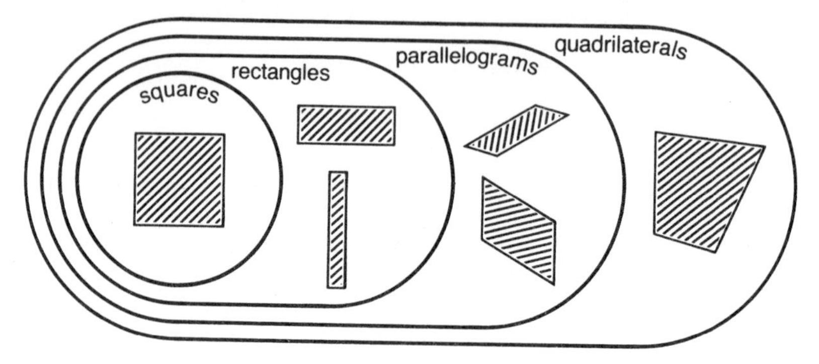


Figure 7

(*iii*) Surface areas of solid shapes. The children will have considered what shape 'nets' various solids have by unfolding boxes and then folding them back up together. But they are unlikely to have considered the question of surface area at that early stage. This is best introduced by making and unmaking a number of cubes, so that it is clear how the surface area can be calculated without it being necessary to unwrap the net (Figure 8).

The children can then be asked to apply this theory to other solid shapes. Thus they can calculate the surface area of a tetrahedron or a prism and can then check their answers by unfolding one and calculating the areas of the various faces. This type of activity reinforces the concepts of faces and edges and vertices or corners. Children can be encouraged to think out how many faces different solids have. This can lead to the discovery of Euler's theorem – that the number of vertices plus the number of faces minus the number of edges is equal to 2 – for this type of solid ($V + F - E = 2$). Children seem to get quite a kick out of trying out this formula on a number of different and complicated solids. Another useful activity involving faces and surface area is to imagine that a box of specified volume (e.g. 72 cm) is to be given as a present, and it can be made in any cuboid that is chosen. However, the box is going to be dipped in

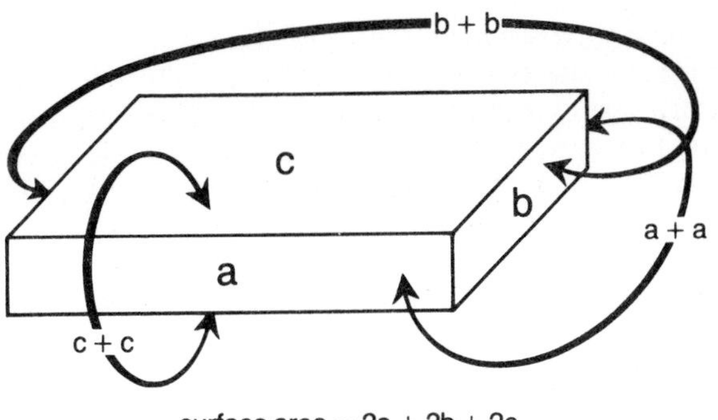


Figure 8

liquid gold so that it becomes very important to maximize the surface area. What is the maximum surface area that can be achieved for a volume of 72 cm, in the shape of a cuboid? Suppose the question were to allow a volume of 64 cm, or 96 cm? This can easily become a mini-investigation, with children setting their own further problems, hypothesizing, and making predictions.

(*iv*) The volumes of solids. Volume, as was stated in chapter 7, is not a matter of formulae. It needs to be taught in a very practical way. The children should have done (and continue to do) a lot of work on volume and capacity. They can fill cubic, cuboid and cylindrical boxes with liquids and measure their capacity before measuring the edges in order to multiply one edge by another. To assist any child who is uncertain about the rationale behind the multiplication of edges, there is a useful activity which involves building up a given volume by constructing layer upon layer of small blocks or centi-cubes (Figure 9).

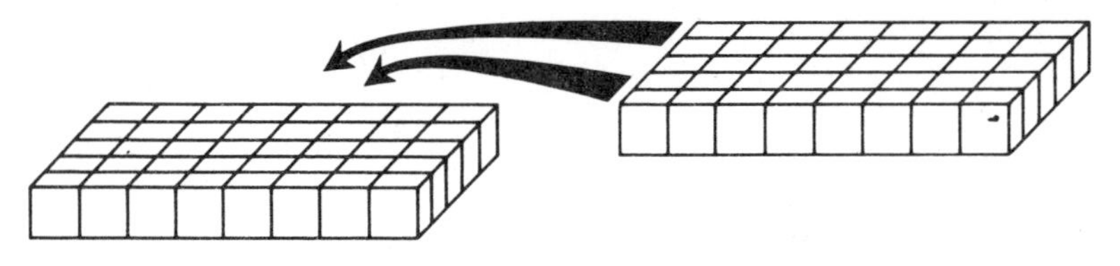

Figure 9

This helps develop the sense of area as a number of rows of columns, and of volume as layers of rows of columns. Once the child has the idea of volume as layers, then the notion of a uniform cross-section follows naturally. A solid of uniform cross-section has a volume which is easily calculated because it consists of a number of layers of circles as in a cylinder, or a number of layers of triangles as in a pyramid, or a number of layers of squares or oblongs as in a cuboid (Figure 10).

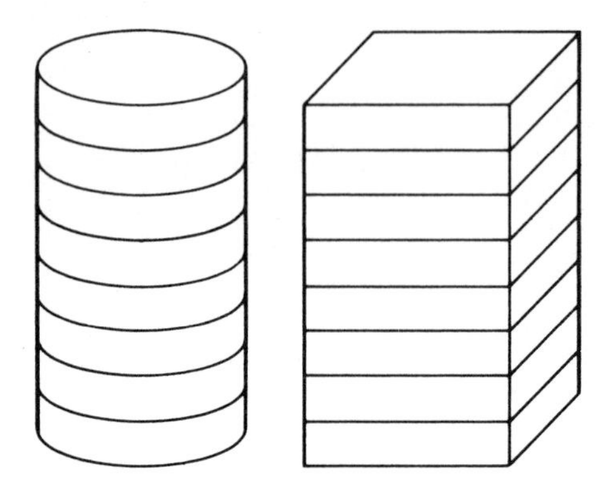

Figure 10

(*v*) Cubes and cubic numbers. Just as the children built up the idea of squares and square numbers, so they can now come to understand the similar idea of cubes and cubic numbers. Build a series of cubes out of Multilink. There are a number of ways of doing this: open; closed; and strutted (Figure 11). It has to be pointed out to the children that the cubic numbers are the ones which are achieved when the closed sort of cubes are built. The children can then see if they can obtain a series of 'pyramid' numbers in a similar fashion. They can also investigate the difference between the cubic numbers and ascertain what series that produces.

(*vi*) Using a pinboard, children can investigate other 2-dimensional shapes. They can experiment to see if they can spot how many different kinds of hexagon, etc. they can find. Once the children have played around with shapes a great deal, they can start comparing one 2-dimensional shape with another. This may lead to the realization that an octagon may be formed by adding a triangle on to a heptagon, etc. (Figure 12).

The children can also measure the angles of regular shapes with increasing numbers of sides and see what pattern emerges: an equilateral triangle has angles of 60°, a square has angles of 90°, a pentagon has angles of 108°. This helps children to explore more fully the properties of different polygons, and also to discover something about the relations between them.

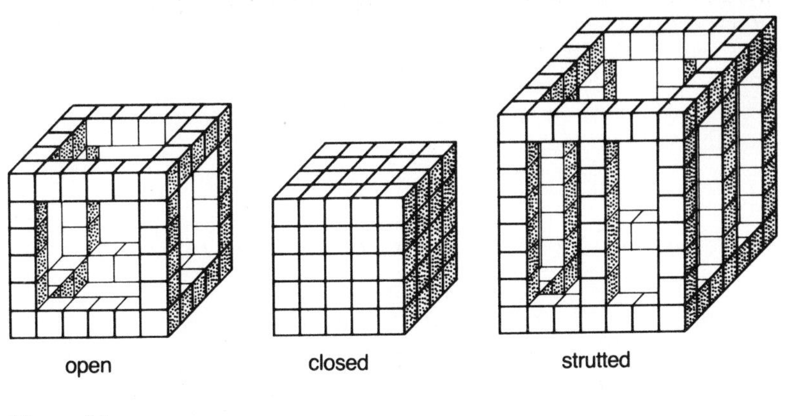


Figure 11

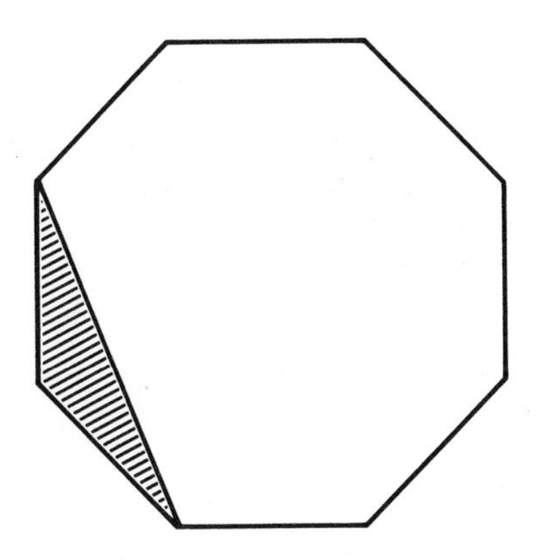

Figure 12

**Investigations involving shape**

All the investigations outlined below are open-ended. Most of them do not have one easy and obvious solution. They can all be continued by asking 'What if . . .?' at almost any stage. Some of them are really quite long and all of them are best approached by pairs or small groups of children rather than by individuals. Since quite a few of these particular investigations involve quite a lot of drawing at the collecting of data stages, it is much faster and more efficient to work together in small groups and thereby to spread out the more tedious drawing and data collection. All the investigations below can be done at any level, from second or third year juniors to adults on in-service courses. They all require and develop the investigative skills of sorting and classifying information, hypothesizing, predicting, testing and demonstrating. With one or two of them it is even possible to construct a proof!

(*i*) Is it possible for a pentagon to have 2 or 3 or even 4 right angles? What about a hexagon? Is there a pattern? Is it possible to predict the maximum number of right angles possible in an octagon?

(*ii*) What is the minimum number of sides a polygon with 3 reflex angles must have? And one with 4? Is there a pattern?

(*iii*) A regular hexagon has 3 pairs of parallel sides, a square has 2. Is it possible for a hexagon to have 3 sides parallel to each other? What about other polygons? Does it make any difference if the number of sides is even or odd? Investigate parallel sides in polygons, regular and irregular.

(*iv*) Polyominoes. The first four types of polyomino are set out (Figure 13).

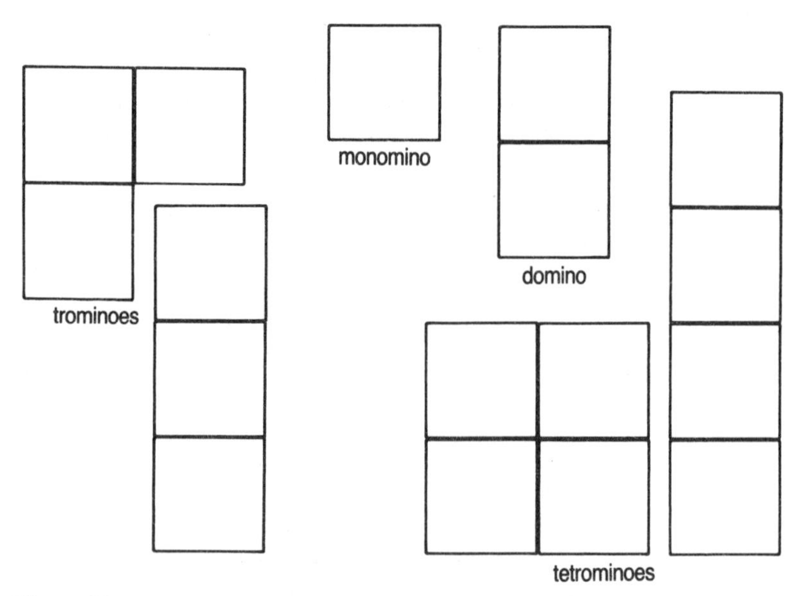

Figure 13

How many different tetrominoes are there? How many different pentominoes? Is it possible to get sufficiently far to be able to predict?

(*v*) Tesselating polyominoes. Which of the polyominoes outlined in the investigation above, will tesselate. Which tetrominoes tesselate? Which pentominoes tesselate? Is there a pattern?

## Topology

By the time they reach junior school, children will have a good working understanding of the basic topological ideas because they are operating with them in their ordinary lives. Some of these notions can now be formalized and made explicit so that we can reflect upon the relationships involved.

### Topological drawings, networks or maps

(*i*) Nodes. Nodes are what we referred to loosely as junctions in chapter 10. They are points which have at least 1 route leading to them. The order of a node is the number of routes leading to it. Earlier, children generally thought of nodes as junctions and therefore imagined them as having at least 2 routes leading to them, but in fact, the limiting case of a node is that of a point with just 1 route leading to or from it (Figure 14). However, it is most useful for children to stick with junctions and to think of a junction as a point that has 2 or more routes meeting there. This is a concept which

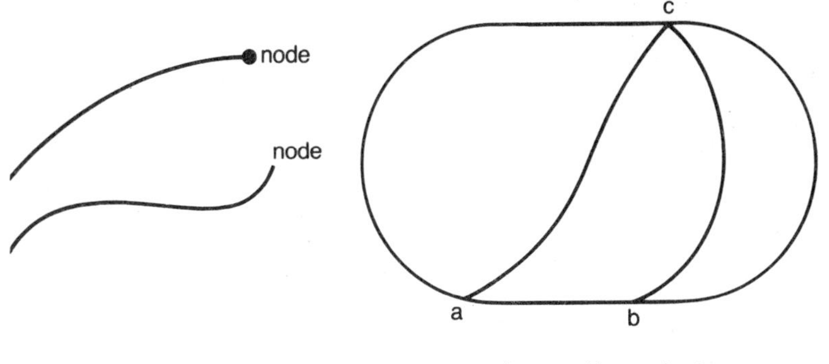


Figure 14

links well with any work that the children have done on maps or plans and they will not find it difficult to grasp.

(*ii*) Arcs. An arc is a route or a line which joins 2 nodes. It can always be drawn with 1 continuous line and is sometimes referred to as a route. A route is circular if, in following the whole distance it traverses, one returns to the starting point.

(*iii*) Regions. A region is a space bounded by 1 or more than 1 route, but the space outside a figure is also a region. Children can have great fun counting and colouring regions and junctions on scribble patterns. They scribble on a piece of paper, drawing 1 continuous route that crosses and re-crosses itself many times. The children then count the numbers of junctions, routes and regions. They can also colour this pattern using the minimum number of colours possible (it can't be more than 4!).

(*iv*) Networks. A network is a diagram or a design or a pattern made up of junctions, routes and regions. No network needs more than 4 colours to colour it (see chapter 10).

(*v*) Traversable networks. A network is said to be traversable if it can be drawn without taking the pen away from the page, and without going over the same route twice.

(*vi*) Transformations. One shape in topology can be transformed into another if it only involves bending or stretching to do so. It is not transformable if it involves cutting or joining. Thus the numbers of arcs, regions and nodes must stay the same.

(*vii*) Topological equivalence. The networks are equivalent in topology if they are transformable, one into the other.

## 3-dimensional topology

It is fun and illuminating for children to play with the 3-dimensional topological ideas and probably the most bizarre and memorable of these is the Moebius Ring. This was invented by a mathematician who is sometimes referred to as the father of modern topology, a German astronomer called Ferdinand Moebius (1790–1868). The ring is a 3-dimensional solid figure which has only one side.

(*i*) How to make the Moebius Ring. Take a strip of paper. Give it one twist and join the ends. Now colour one side of it. This should mean that you colour the whole ring without stopping or going over the edge. This ring has only one side.

(*ii*) Variations using the Moebius Ring. Cut the ring all along the middle in one continuous line. How many rings do you now have? Repeat this performance. Now how many rings are there? What about a third and fourth cut? This is a topological investigation and some children will become so intrigued that they will want to tabulate their results and explore further.

There are many other enjoyable and almost magical activities using topology. These include some famous puzzles such as the Koenigsberg bridges problem (Figure 15), and the gas, electricity and water to all 3 houses problem (Figure 16). Topology is a topic which can be immense fun in the primary school and which leads on to some very interesting new mathematical ideas at a later stage.

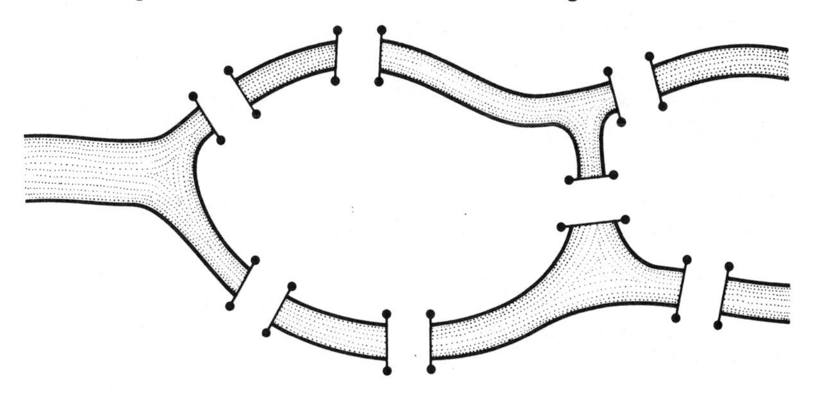

Koenigsberg Bridges

Can a walk be devised which crosses each bridge once and only once?

Figure 15

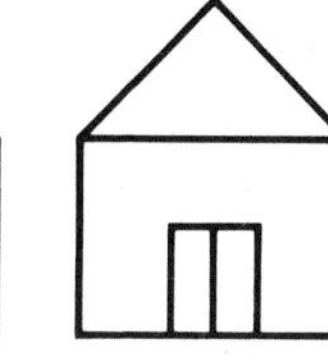

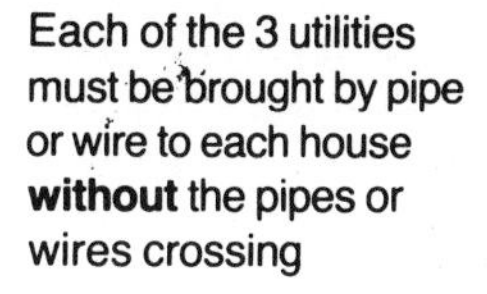

Figure 16

# 12

# Symmetry, patterns and rotation leading to angle

## Symmetry

Notions of symmetry are fundamental. Seeing that something is or is not symmetrical can be of great mathematical importance. Certain mathematical laws follow from certain hypothesized symmetries of the universe. It is, therefore, important that children come to acquire a sense of symmetry as early as possible.

The whole idea of symmetry consists of the notion that things can be moved around and still look the same. With children we start with the idea of line symmetry and progress later to a notion of rotational symmetry.

### Line symmetry

Children often seem to possess an almost instinctive understanding of what it means for a thing to be symmetrical. When they build models, arrange objects or draw patterns they frequently take pains to achieve a symmetrical result. However, they may not have reflected much on this process and are often not familiar with the language involved, nor are they aware of the mathematical implications.

Some activities which help develop a sense of symmetry include:

(*i*) Name symmetry. Fold a piece of paper in half and draw a line about 1 cm above the fold. Draw a name along the line in large thick letters (Figure 1). Carefully cut around the letters or alternatively cut the letters out. Open up the paper and mount it on a contrasting colour. With children who are too young to manage the cutting skills, the same activity can be done with just their initial so that they can cut out 'their' letter.

(*ii*) 'Holes' symmetry. You will need a piece of black sugar paper and some brightly-coloured tissue paper. Fold the black paper in half and cut out a pattern of holes. Open it up and place overlapping strips of tissue paper along the back of the black paper covering the holes and stick them into place. A stained glass effect can be achieved by sticking the result on to the classroom window.

Figure 1

*(iii)* Squared paper symmetry. Fold a piece of squared paper in half. Cut out a shape. Open it up and colour it with several colours so that it is entirely symmetrical. This can be made into a more structured activity by asking the children to make a symmetrical robot or an animal or some named object so that they have to be more thoughtful about the cutting out.

*(iv)* Sewing symmetry. Using binca, children can sew a symmetrical pattern. As it seems to be easier for children to design a pattern which is set within fairly strict parameters, it is helpful to suggest limits within which their design must be situated. Thus, 'design a symmetrical vehicle pattern', or 'design a symmetrical flower pattern', is often easier than a more open-ended demand. Children can stitch their patterns using cross-stitch or any other suitable stitch and can border it if desired.

*(v)* Building models. Ask the children to build a symmetrical model out of Lego or Multilink. This is quite a demanding task for small children since they have to think in terms of 3 dimensions. This activity also involves a great deal of mathematical language as the children construct their models and turn them round to look at them from various different directions to check whether or not they are symmetrical.

*(vi)* Symmetrical dancing dolls. This activity is one which many children may have done at home and in the playgroup. It utilizes some of the ideas we are presently trying to develop. Take a piece of

paper and concertina it up neatly as if making a fan. Draw and cut out one half of a figure. When the paper is opened up there is a row of little dancing figures, all perfectly symmetrical (Figure 2).

Figure 2

(*vii*) Blob/string prints. With very small children as well as with older ones, strange and beautiful patterns can be made using the technique of blob or string printing. You will need thick luminous paints or very bright primary colours and some cheerful matching paper.

To do blob prints place several blobs of colour on one side of a sheet of paper. Fold it over and smooth it down with your fingers. When this is opened up, a pattern, which is symmetrical about the fold, should appear. By controlling the movements of their fingers when smoothing out the paints the children can achieve some rather spectacular effects.

String painting involves the same technique but this time, instead of putting blobs of paint on one side of the paper, a piece of string which has been dipped in paint is curled up on that side of the paper with one end left hanging over the edge. Fold over the paper and with one hand pull out the string while the other holds the paper down (Figure 3). Many children like the sensation of the string moving under their hand as it is gently pulled out and a strange and symmetrical pattern appears when the paper is unfolded. More colours can be added by repeating the process.

(*viii*) Sorting symmetrical shapes. It is quite a demanding task to ask small children to sort a pile of shapes, both 2-dimensional and solid, into symmetrical and non-symmetrical shapes. The 2-dimen-

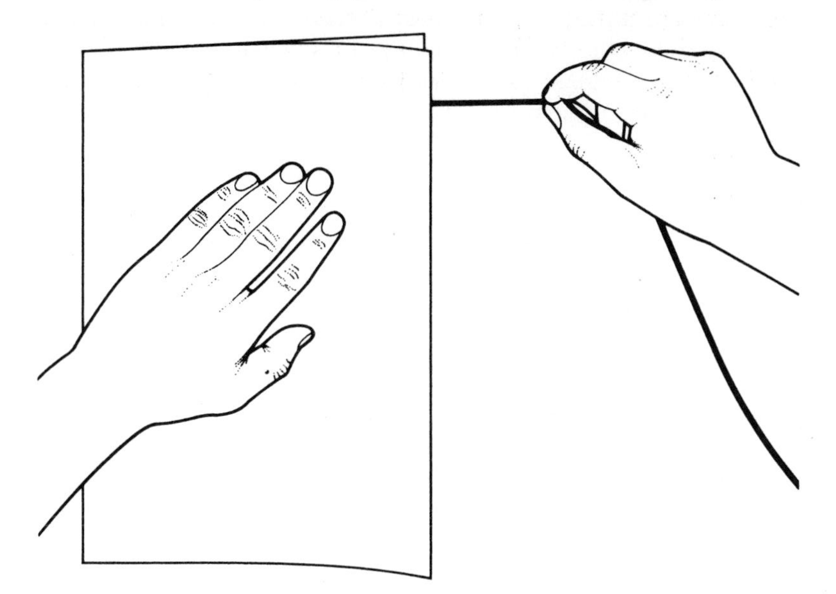

Figure 3

sional ones are not always obvious; a circle, for example, often gives problems as there is no obvious line about which it is symmetrical. Some shapes can be irregular but symmetric (Figure 4).

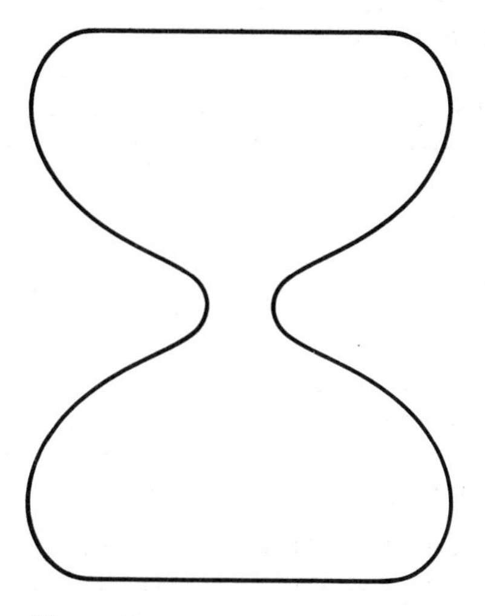

Figure 4

When the children are small they will be looking principally for line symmetry but there is also rotational symmetry, and some shapes have rotational symmetry but not line (Figure 5). When dealing with line or mirror symmetry such shapes do not count.

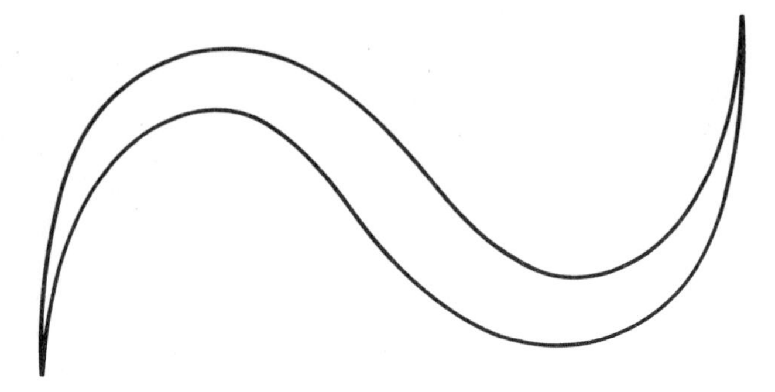

Figure 5

**Rotational symmetry**

Even some quite mature children find rotational symmetry difficult to grasp. The basic idea is that of seeing if an object still looks the same when it has been turned round. One way to test this is to take, for example, a single, coloured square. The children look at the square and then shut their eyes. With the same side still facing the chidlren, the square is turned to right or left through a quarter turn. When the children open their eyes, can they tell if it has been turned or not? In the case of a square and one quarter turn it looks exactly as it did before, therefore it is said to have rotational symmetry of order 4. If it had been turned through one eighth of a turn then it would have ended up standing on one corner and it would not have looked the same, so a square does not have rotational symmetry of order 8.

Activities to develop the idea of rotational symmetry include:

(*i*) Carbon symmetry. You will need a piece of thin flimsy paper, a biro and a piece of carbon paper per child. Put the flimsy against the carbon side and fold them in half with the flimsy on the outside. Fold in half again and then along the diagonal (Figure 6).
At this stage a pretty edge may be made by cutting as shown in Figure 6. Pressing very hard, draw a simple pattern on the outside of the folded paper. When the paper is opened up and the carbon removed, a pattern with rotational symmetry order 8 should appear. The patterns can be gone over and each segment coloured in. Collectively, they will make a lovely display.

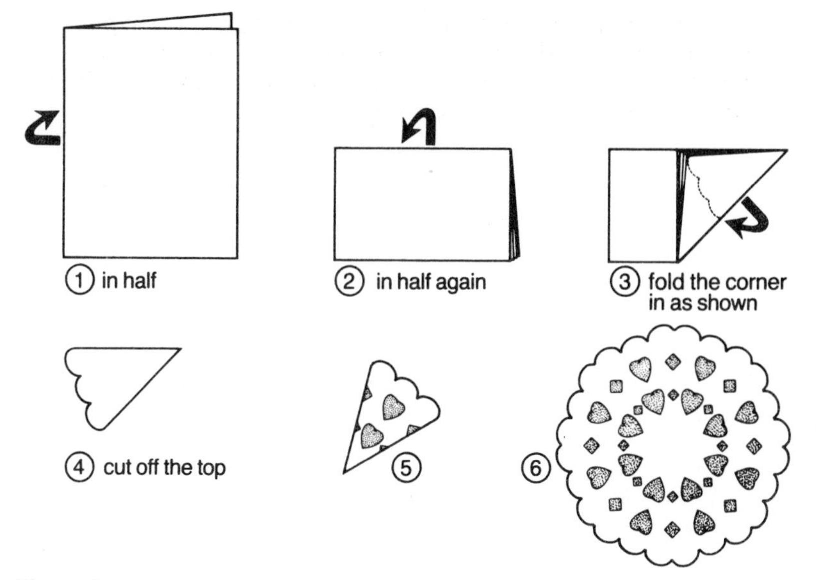


Figure 6

(*ii*) Rotating prints. Use paper prints to make a pattern with rotational symmetry. Cut out a shape from a piece of sugar paper (or tear out the shape if slightly blurred edges to the print are preferred). Place a dot on one corner of the print and another in the middle of a clean piece of paper. Place the shape on the paper with the two dots together. Using a wax crayon shade gently all round the edge of the shape to give an outline on the page. Keeping the two dots together rotate the shape and repeat the process. Continue to do this until the shape has rotated through a complete circle (Figure 7). The activity can be extended by drawing round a shape rather than printing. A child could obtain a circle of squares in this way.

(*iii*) Looking for symmetry in the world around. Of course, any study of patterns will inevitably result in children noticing a great deal that is symmetrical in the world around them. Wallpaper patterns can be classified into 17 basic symmetry groups and it is alleged that all 17 appear in the decorative work in the Moorish palace, the Alhambra.

Children can study the world around them and pick out those shapes which are symmetrical and those which are not. Road signs make an excellent resource here. Children can find out what they mean, discuss how effective each sign is in graphical terms and look at it to decide whether or not it is symmetrical: What are the advantages of making road signs symmetrical?

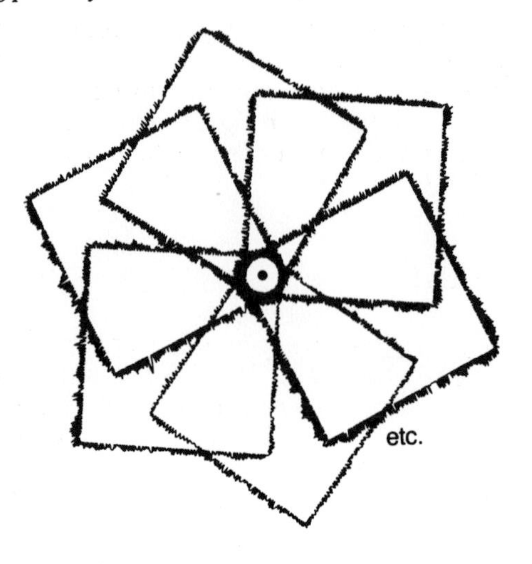


Figure 7

The letters of the alphabet are another useful resource here. It is a demanding exercise for older children to study the alphabet and decide which letters are, and which are not, symmetrical, and in what way.

*(iv)* Palindromic numbers. Palindromic numbers are numbers which are symmetrical, that is to say they read the same forwards or backwards (e.g. 737). This parallels the definition of a palindrome which is a word which reads the same forwards or backwards (e.g. LEVEL. There are also palindromic sentences (WAS IT A CAT I SAW) and phrases (A MAN, A PLAN, A CANAL, PANAMA). Just as children can make up whole palindromic sentences so they can make up palindromic number sentences: $3 \times 4 = 4 \times 3$

Here is a way of generating palindromic numbers:

Take a number – 346
Reverse the digits – 643
Add – 989

The answer is a palindrome. Sometimes it takes a while before the palindrome is achieved but the method of reversing the digits and adding, reversing them again and adding, is always the same.

## Angle

Children find the concept of angle a difficult one, particularly if the subject is never mentioned until one day a teacher throws a protractor at them in the secondary school and asks them to measure an angle. Of course, with the development of Logo, many children are using the idea of angles much earlier and in a more concrete situation but it still tends to be a notion which is generally neglected in primary mathematics.

## Basic angle work

Small children must see angle as a measurement of the amount of turn or rotation. First they can look around and notice and list all those things which turn: door handles, clock hands, heads, eyes, wheels, water taps, knobs on cookers and television sets, and so on. With reception-age children, simply getting them to notice and comment on those things which can turn will help them reflect on the idea of turning.

Once they have grasped the notion that many things do turn, we can develop the concept of measuring the amount of turn. This can be introduced in a number of ways including:

(*i*) Two interlocking circles. The two interlocking circles have already come in useful when teaching 'time' (see chapter 8). Cut two circles with the same radius out of different coloured paper. Cut them along a radius and interlock them one with another. The underneath circle can now be rotated slowly through the 'on top' circle to demonstrate an ever-increasing angle being created (Figure 8). If each child makes one of these small devices it helps them remember that measuring angles means measuring the amount of turn something makes. They can demonstrate to their own satisfaction a quarter turn, a half turn and three-quarters of a turn.

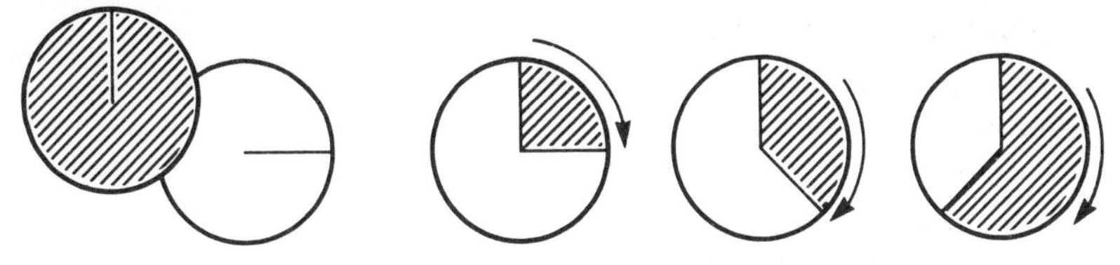


Figure 8

(*ii*) Right angles. Once the concept of angle as a 'turning' is firmly established, children can look for, recognize and classify particular angles. One of the most common, and certainly the easiest to recognize and estimate, is a right angle. Right angles appear everywhere; there are always examples immediately to hand in or out of the primary classroom. Children can also demonstrate an approximate, right angle for themselves using either two fingers or their arm (Figure 9). Helping the children to develop a real sense of what a right angle is and how to estimate one is most useful as a precursor to the next activity and many others.

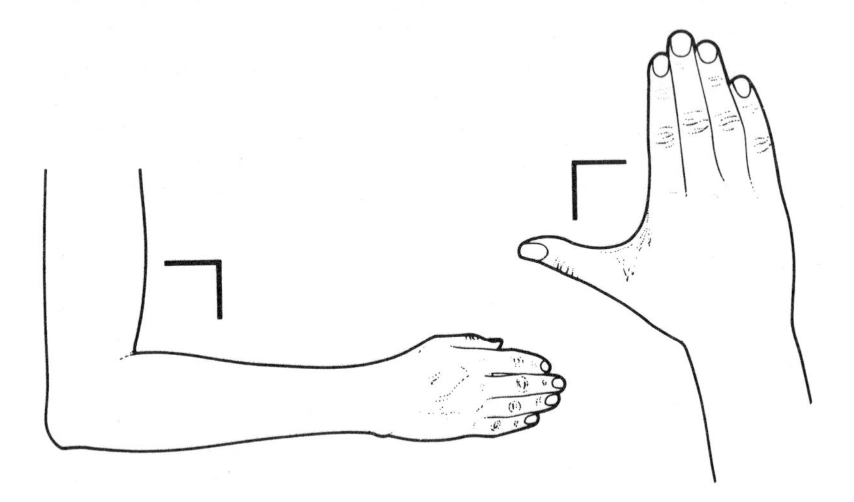

Figure 9

(*iii*) Human robot. Take one child and instruct him or her to be a human robot. This robot may only do what it is programmed (told) to do; it may not think for itself! The other children must 'program' the human robot to walk up to and around a piece of furniture placed in the middle of the room without bumping into it or going too far away from it. Thus the children must estimate the distance the robot must walk in paces, then instruct it how to turn, how much and in which direction, in order to negotiate a route around the piece of furniture. There are other things that the robot can be asked to do, such as to pace out a particular shape on the floor.

These activities are the natural precursors of Logo: once children are able to understand angle as the amount of turn, they can relate much more quickly and easily to Logo.

(*iv*) Points of the compass. Children can use the compass – north, east, south and west – in order to help them develop the concept of angle and skill in adding or subtracting angles. A child can be required to give 6 instructions to turn to face different directions, ending up facing north, for example. The children can also give directions to walk along a known route using the points of the compass. They could also use the same system to get someone else to write their name by remote control. By way of example: go north 5 paces; turn east; walk 2 paces; turn through 2 right-angles to face west; walk four paces; turn through 2 right-angles to face east; walk 2 paces; turn south; walk 5 paces. (This spells 'T'.) Thinking out instructions such as these is very useful and reinforces all the ideas about angles and right-angles in particular.

(*v*) The idea of turning and angles can also be developed through the use of Logo on a microcomputer. The software is fairly easy to use and many children can get very enthusiastic about drawing patterns on the screen and moving turtles around the floor. Control technology, or the practice of controlling machines and machinery using the microcomputer, also involves children having to turn through various size angles.

## Measuring angles

By the time the children come, later on in the junior school, to use protractors in order to measure angles, they should have a very good sense of what an angle is. A child of 9 or 10 should be able to estimate whether an angle is more than 90° (obtuse), less than 90° (acute) or exactly 90° (a right angle) (Figure 10). They should be able to count the number of angles in a figure and give a rough idea of their sum. As for angles in degrees, there is some dispute as to how accurately primary-age children should be able to measure using this unit. Up until third year juniors or thereabouts, the children will be operating by talking of quarter and half turns and even of half of quarter turns and one eighth of a turn. When degrees are introduced, the children might be interested to know that the Babylonians, believing that the time it took the sun to go right round the earth was 360 days, decided to divide the circle into 360 degrees.

Useful questions and activities to assist in developing measurement in degrees include:

(*i*) How many degrees are there in a right angle? How many degrees are there between South and South West on a compass? How many degrees does the minute hand on a clock move in going from five o'clock to five past the hour?

Allowing children to play with compasses and watch hands, to draw the angles they make and then to calculate the number of

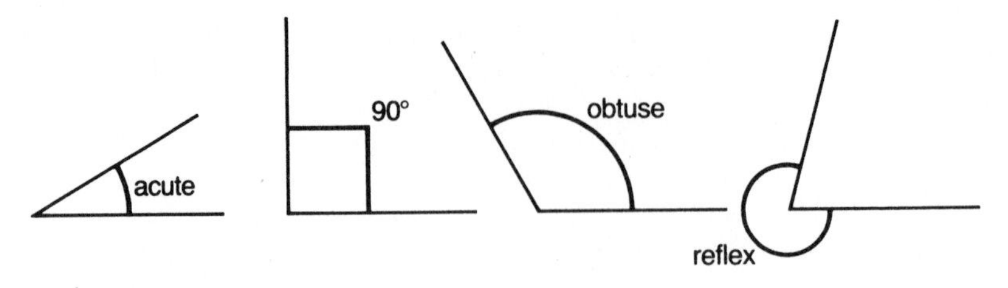


Figure 10

degrees makes a very useful introduction to using a protractor to measure degrees.

(*ii*) Children can be asked to draw angles, first of all of approximately a certain size and then to check the measurement using a protractor. They can then draw accurate angles of a given size using the protractor.

## Angles in polygons

(*i*) Angles in triangles. Children will normally know that there are 3 angles in a triangle. It can be quickly and effectively demonstrated that these 3 angles add up to 180°. Cut out any triangle from a piece of paper and colour each of the angles on it in a different colour. Cut out the angles, or fold them in to the middle so that they touch, if they will reach (Figure 11). The 3 angles will fit together to form a straight line. Demonstrate that a straight line is 2 right angles or 180°. Thus the 3 angles of a triangle have been shown to add up to 180°.

(*ii*) Angles in a quadrilateral. Once again, children are mostly aware that a quadrilateral has 4 angles. The demonstration that the 4 angles always add up to 360° is very similar to the one described above. Draw any quadrilateral. Colour all the angles in different colours. Tear them out and arrange them so that they form a complete circle. This is known to be one complete rotation or 360°.

(*iii*) Angles in any polygon. To establish that when the number of sides of a polygon is increased by 1 the sum of its angles is increased by 180°, it is necessary to enable children to see that adding one side to a polygon is tantamount to adding a triangle. This can most easily be done on a pinboard or by drawing a triangle on to a polygon. Plastic or paper shapes can also be moved around to obtain new polygons.

Another effective way of establishing this notion is to adopt an

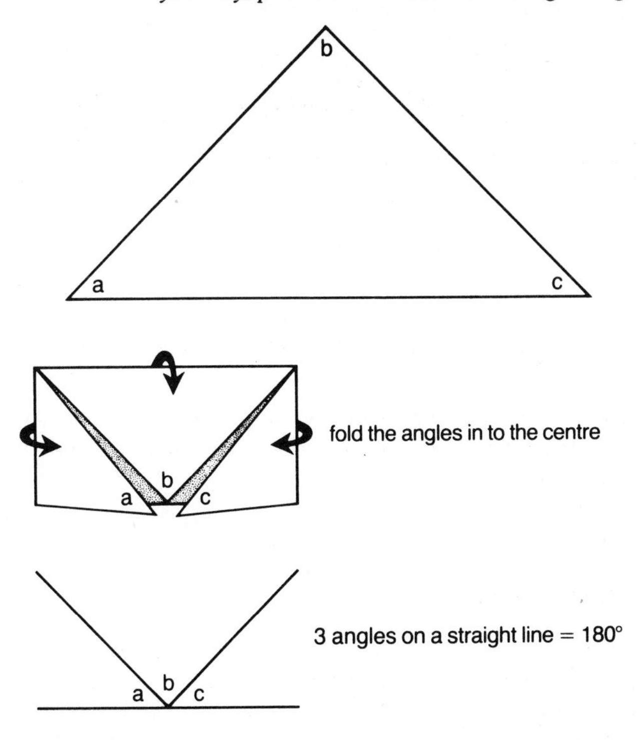


Figure 11

investigative approach and require the children to draw a pentagon, cut out the angles as before and arrange them in a circle and then on round; they cover 540°. They can repeat the process with any hexagon and so on until it is clear that the sum of the angles increases by 180° each time the number of sides of the polygon increases by 1.

# 13

# Co-ordinates and graphs

## Co-ordinates

### Introducing co-ordinates

Co-ordinate work forms the basis for much of the graph work done in primary school. There are two skills involved. The first is the ability to read across and down – the same skill which is required for reading a timetable. The second is the realization that any point in a plane can be identified by means of an ordered pair of numbers.

Primary maths schemes for use in schools vary in their approach to the introduction of the subject. Some schemes start by developing the first of the two skills outlined. They teach the children to read along and down, or up, by numbering the *squares* on a grid. Other schemes take the view that from the start it is the *lines* which should be numbered and also their intersections which the children have to come to see as important in isolating a point in a plane. Although the latter approach may appeal to purists in mathematics, the former has the practical advantage that it makes concrete links with any work done involving block graphs. It also connects with work done on addition, subtraction and number squares which relies on the acquisition of similar skills (see chapters 3 and 4).

Some ideas for the development of early co-ordinate work are:

(*i*) Draw a pair of axes and number the lines along the $x$ axis and up the $y$ axis. Ask the children to choose an 'address' on the grid, for example, Harry could be at (3, 4) and Julie at (2, 5). The children can plot their own addresses, remembering that the first number gives the position along the $x$ axis and the second gives the position up the $y$ axis. A useful phrase in this context is: 'along the corridor and up the stairs'. Once the children have plotted their own 'addresses' they can plot those of their friends on the same grid. They can also invent 'addresses' for fictional characters, (0, 7) might be James Bond's address (Figure 1).

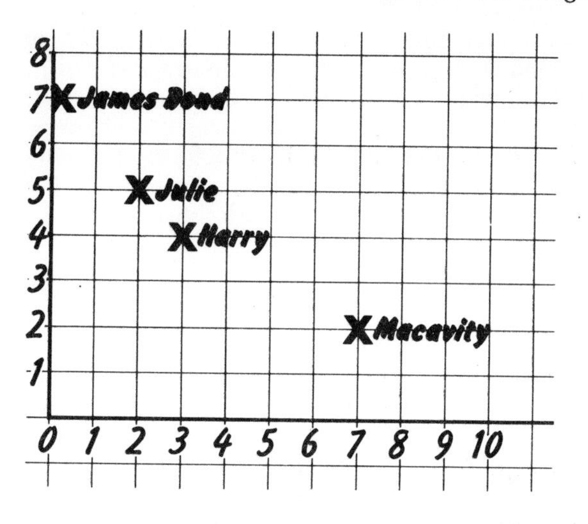


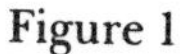
Figure 1

(*ii*) Using a similar grid, children can plot the points necessary to draw the initial letter of their name (Figure 2). This activity involves the children in connecting points on a graph rather than plotting isolated points.

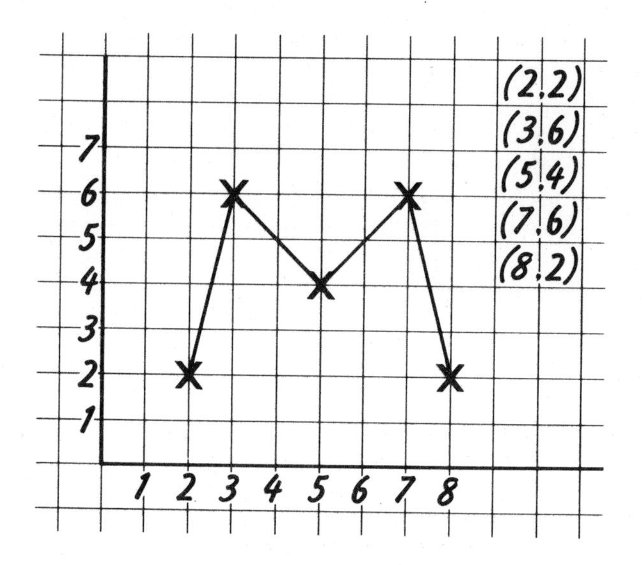


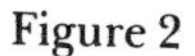
Figure 2

(*iii*) Children can experiment with plotting points, writing down their co-ordinates, reversing the co-ordinates and plotting the new points on their grid. This will emphasize for children the ordering aspects of co-ordinates, that it *matters* which way round they are written – (3, 2) is *not* the same point as (2,3). Co-ordinates form an ordered pair and children should be aware of the necessity of remembering which co-ordinate comes first and which comes second and the difference between them.

(*iv*) Ask the children to draw a shape on their grid, list the co-ordinates of the points necessary to draw it and give the list of co-ordinates, without the picture, to a friend who must then draw the shape using only the list of co-ordinates. This is a much harder activity than it seems. Occasionally it is necessary to write some additional instructions to clarify the order in which the points must be joined. However, it is an activity which children enjoy very much and one which encourages co-operative learning since the work is done in pairs or groups.

(*v*) Co-ordinate battleships. Children can play either version of battleships outlined below. The first version relies upon positioning the ships and submarines in the spaces on a grid. The second version positions the ships and submarines on the intersection of the lines. In both versions the main point of the game is to eliminate your opponent's ships. Each player places several ships, submarines and aircraft carriers on their grid, the exact number and size (2 points/squares, 3, 4, 5 points/squares) of the vessels being agreed before the game begins (Figure 3). Having positioned the ships each player draws out an empty grid on which they plot the co-ordinates at which they 'shoot' on their opponent's grid. The game proceeds with each player taking it in turn to shoot three shots at the other's grid. The shots must be on adjacent points/squares. The player being shot at marks the co-ordinates targeted on their grid and must tell their opponent if anything has been hit. The winner is the player who first sinks all the opponent's vessels.

The game gives excellent practice in plotting points and reading a grid and children of all ages enjoy it.

(*vi*) Co-ordinate 'four-in-a-line'. In this game each player requires a marked and numbered grid; the lines but not the spaces are numbered. Each player throws a dice twice, the numbers thus obtained produce a pair of co-ordinates which are plotted on the player's grid. The next player then throws the dice and plots the point on their grid. The winner is the first person to obtain 4 adjacent points in a line in any direction. If the game is too long it can be changed to require only 3 in a line to win.

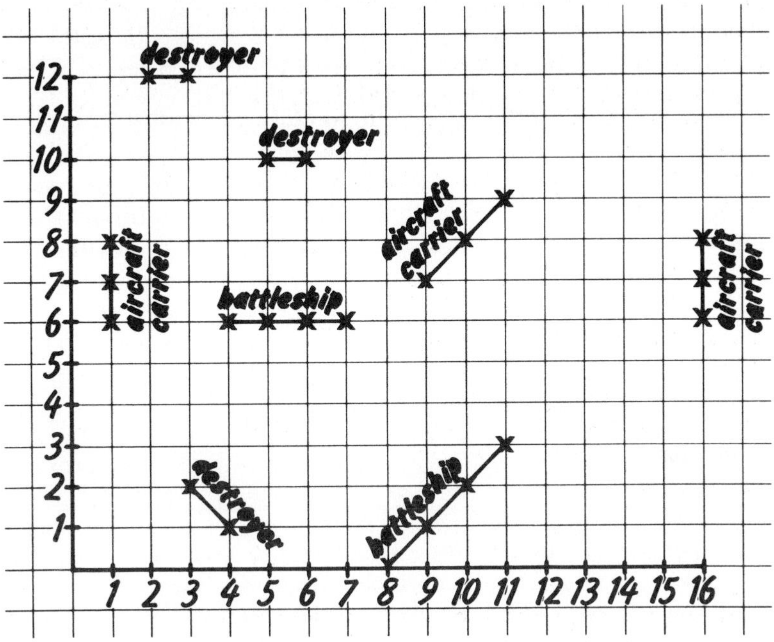

Figure 3

**Maps and co-ordinate work**

Reading all types of maps and street plans depends upon being able to read a grid. Street plans generally rely upon naming or numbering the spaces whilst ordnance survey maps number and letter the lines. This means that work with maps, which can arise in other areas of the curriculum, is very helpful in developing the idea of co-ordinates.

(*i*) Let the children draw their own map of a treasure island on a grid, including features like hills, forts, rivers, buried treasure. They are then asked to give the co-ordinates of these places which act as map references for the features identified. The co-ordinates of the treasure can be kept secret and friends can be asked to guess the position of the treasure.

The drawing of a map like this is obviously best done as a part of a topic or project in which the children are already involved.

(*ii*) Street plans. The children can draw a street plan of a neighbourhood which they know well, making their own grid the purpose. As on the London and other A–Z plans, it is useful if they number the spaces rather than the lines. They can increase the similarity between their own street plan and the real thing by using letters along the $x$ axis and numbers down the $y$ axis or vice versa.

The actual drawing of a street plan by this method is surprisingly difficult and the preparation for it may involve children pacing the streets, using compasses and performing all sorts of measurements and estimates. The accuracy and amount of detail on the plan will depend upon the age of the children and their familiarity with the area.

(*iii*) Reproduce a section of an ordnance survey map and use it to do co-ordinate activities. This activity should arise out of a project so that the map is not just produced out of the air but is seen in the context of other work and thus has a realistic and definite purpose. The children can then be asked to mark things on the map at particular named points. They can also be required to read off the map and say what feature appears at a particular reference. Most children, recognizing the practical advantages of the exercise, enjoy this aspect of learning about co-ordinates and the skills learned are very useful on school trips, in orienteering and navigation.

All the activities with maps and map-type grids belong within an integrated curriculum. Done on their own, in isolation from their real place within some sort of project, they can appear abstract and much more difficult than they really are. However, when they arise out of project or topic work they provide an excellent means of practising and using co-ordinates and grid-reading skills.

## More complex activities involving co-ordinates

Once children are clear about how co-ordinates work, some of the preparation for graph work can be done by playing around with co-ordinates and shapes on a graph.

(*i*) Drawing a simple shape and moving it along a graph. The children are asked to plot a few points on their grid and join them up to create a simple shape; they then list the co-ordinates they used. A constant, (not too large – say, 2 or 3) is added to the $x$ co-ordinate (the $x$ co-ordinate is always the first figure in the ordered pair and the $y$ co-ordinate the second). By adding 2 or 3 to every $x$ co-ordinate in the list, a new list of co-ordinates is obtained and when these are plotted on the grid in a different colour, the shape has moved (Figure 4).

Once children have repeated this activity a couple of times, they can try subtracting a constant from each $x$ co-ordinate and plotting

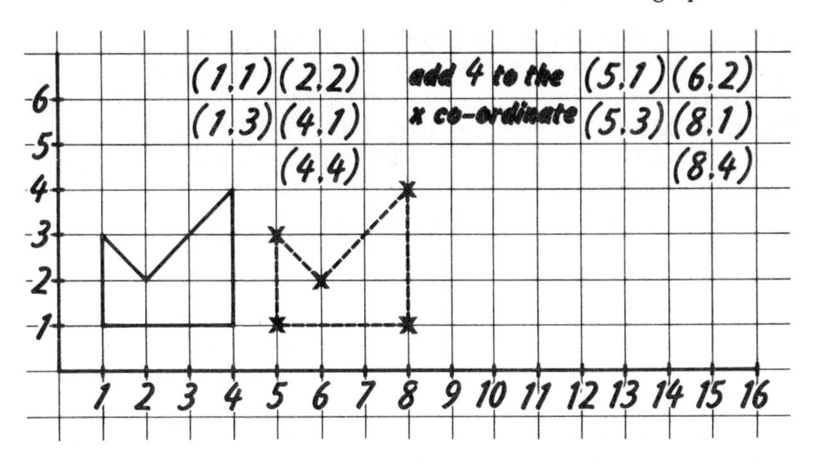


Figure 4

the new position thus obtained.

(*ii*) Drawing a shape and moving it up on a graph. This activity is the same as the previous one except that the constant is added to the $y$ co-ordinate. A simple shape is drawn on the graph and its co-ordinates listed. A constant is added to each $y$ co-ordinate and the new points plotted in a different colour on the graph. This time the shape moves up the graph. How would it be moved down the graph?

(*iii*) Once children are familiar with how a plotted set of co-ordinates, joined to make a shape, can be shifted around a graph in any direction, they can be encouraged to experiment with stretching or enlarging the shapes. Once again they start with very simple shapes, write down the list of co-ordinates and multiply each $x$ co-ordinate by 2, plotting the new co-ordinates on the graph in a different colour. What has happened to the size of the shape? What is the position of the new shape? There is a connection between multiplying by a constant and adding a constant as we did in the first activity in this section. Adding something to the $x$ co-ordinate moved the shape along to the right, multiplying the $x$ co-ordinate by a constant stretches (and moves) the shape along to the right.

(*iv*) Stretching a shape vertically. Many children will now be able to predict that if they multiply the $y$ co-ordinates of a particular shape by a constant the shape will stretch upwards. They must be encouraged to check this theory out by drawing their shape, listing the co-ordinates, doubling the $y$ co-ordinates and plotting the new shape.

(*v*) Enlarging. Once the children have done the previous two activities they can complete the picture by doubling both the co-ordinates of each point on the original shape.

They are now in a position to experiment with enlarging more complex shapes. They can also try reducing shapes by halving the co-ordinates though this may involve fractional co-ordinates.

At that stage children need to play around with different shapes and different grids so that they can find out as much as possible on their own.

(*vi*) Different quadrants. Once the children are familiar with co-ordinate work using positive numbers on a grid, the idea of a pair of axes with negative numbers on them as well can be introduced. This opens up the use of 3 new quadrants on the grid (Figure 5). The children can now experiment with shapes drawn and co-ordinates plotted in each of these quadrants. This will involve the addition and subtraction of negative numbers. The easiest way to view this is to see the axes as number lines and to count forwards or backwards along them accordingly. Thus, if a shape is drawn using the following pairs of co-ordinates: (− 1, 2) (− 1, 4), (− 3, 2) (− 5, 6) and the child wants to move it into the first quadrant, what number must be added to which co-ordinate to achieve this? Some children may find it easiest to work backwards and draw the shape where they want it to end up, write down its new co-ordinates and compare these with the old list to check what has happened.

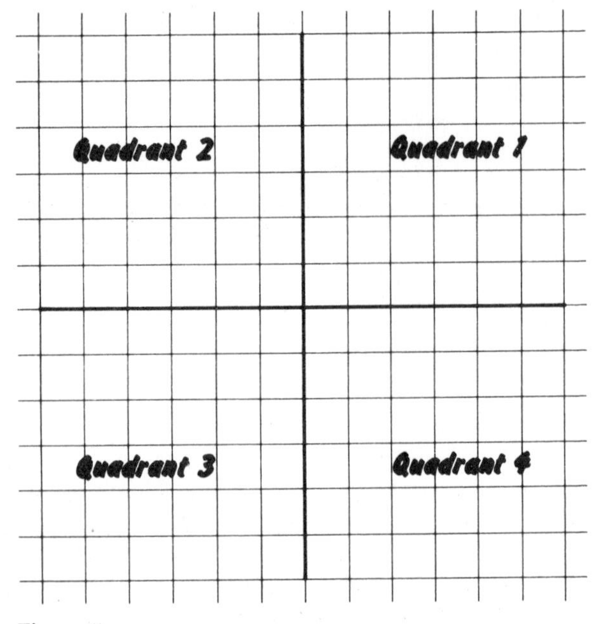


Figure 5

(*vii*) Squaring the co-ordinates. Children can experiment with squaring all the co-ordinates of a shape and seeing what results. This may help them reflect on the process of squaring numbers as it connects with multiplication.

(*viii*) Reflections. Children can draw the line $y = x$ by joining all the points where the $x$ co-ordinate is identical with the $y$ co-ordinate on the grid: (1, 1) (2, 2) (3, 3) etc. This line will then reflect points in it rather as a mirror does. If the point (3, 7) is plotted and then its co-ordinates are reversed the point (7, 3) will be seen to be a reflection of the first. Children can try this out with several pairs of co-ordinates. They can then experiment with reflecting simple shapes in this line (Figure 6).

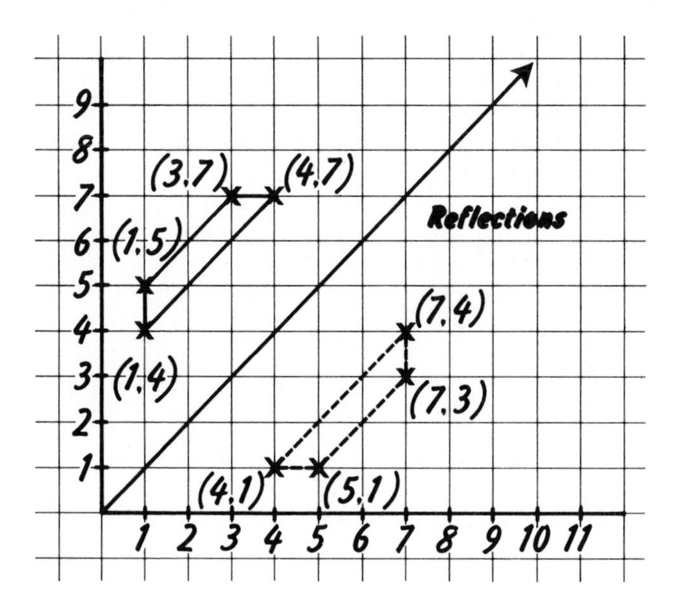


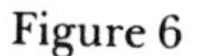
Figure 6

## Early graph work

The more familiar children are with co-ordinates and the more they have practised moving shapes along and around a grid, the less trouble they will have coping with the problems posed by graphs and functions. The sorts of graphs we want children to become familiar with in this context are 'relationship' or 'function' graphs. These become very important later on in secondary and further maths and it is essential that children develop a thorough understanding of the principles involved at the beginning.

(*i*) Draw the lines $x = 3$ and $y = 3$ on a grid. This sounds like an easy task but it is surprising how many children (and adults) have difficulty doing it. The most common error is to plot sloping lines, usually $x = y$, because children think of a line on a graph as having to be a sloping line.

(*ii*) The children can now draw the line $x = y$, which is the line joining all the points where the $x$ co-ordinate is equal to the $y$ co-ordinate. Children should realize that in plotting a straight line there is no necessity to plot more than 3 points, since 2 points give the position and slope of the line and the third point simply acts as a check. This realization is crucial as it saves a lot of time later and it means that children come to understand that although an infinite number of pairs of co-ordinates can be read off a straight line graph, only 3 (or even 2) are needed to be able to draw the line in the first place.

(*iii*) Tables graphs. As was mentioned in chapter 4, some of the easiest relationship graphs to be plotted and drawn are the 'times tables'. Here the $y$ co-ordinate is the product and the $x$ co-ordinate is the number of 7s or 3s or whatever. Thus $y = 3x$ gives the co-ordinate pairs (3, 9) (4, 12) (5, 15) and so on (Figure 7).

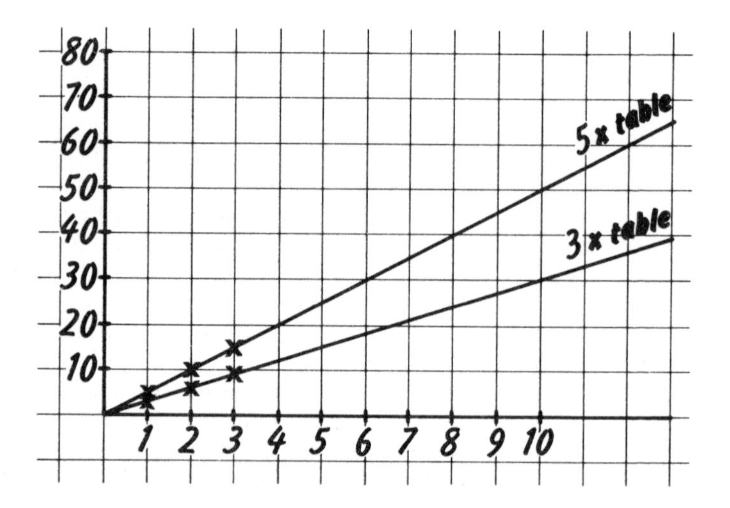


Figure 7

**Functions**

Once the idea of plotting points where there is a constant relationship between the $x$ co-ordinate and the $y$ co-ordinate is grasped, we can make the connection between the graph work and the set theoretic concepts which underlie it.

(*i*) Draw a set of whole numbers under 10 and then think of some simple function to perform which will transform each of those numbers into a new number in a new set (Figure 8).

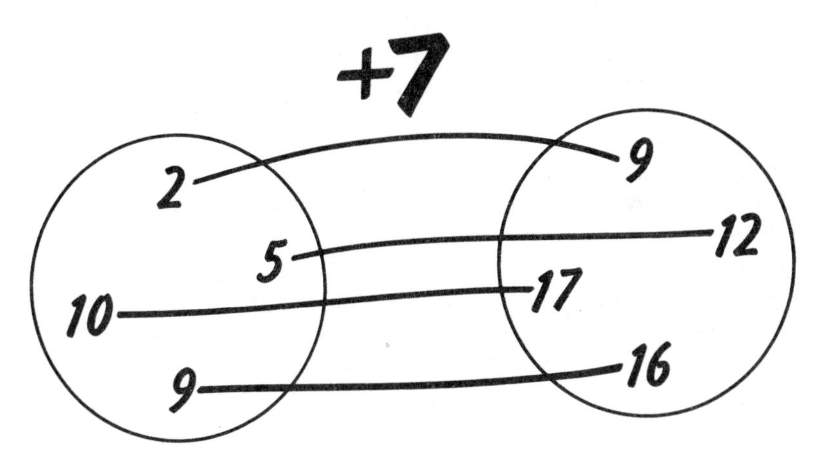


Figure 8

These two sets of numbers, mathematically known as the domain and the target, provide us with the set of ordered pairs which we call co-ordinates and enable us to plot each function, or the relationship between the two sets, on a graph. The easiest way to think of this is by imagining a function as a sort of 'magical box'. You can feed in one number and the box does something to it, and then it comes out as a new number. So if my magical box was 'doubling and adding 1' then if I feed in a 2, I get a 5 out, if I feed in a 4 I get a 9 out and so on.

This idea can be turned into a game called 'guess the rule', where the teacher thinks of a function or 'rule' and the children have to try to guess what it is by feeding her numbers and looking at what happens to them when she applies her 'rule'. So, if I think of multiplying by 3 and subtracting 1, and then the children say '4', I have to reply '11', if they then try '2', I must say '5', and so on until they guess the rule. Children quickly learn that it is good to try '0' and '1' because you get a lot of information that way!

The idea of functions links with graphs since we can draw any function on a graph by using the 2 numbers (the domain and the target) as a pair of co-ordinates. Thus in the example just given, the co-ordinates would be (4, 11), and (2,5).

(*ii*) Pocket money graph. Hilda's pocket money is always twice Fred's plus 3p. Plot the graph of the relationship between Hilda and Fred's pocket money. We can show the relationship as a function which can be written:

Hilda's pocket money = 2 × Fred's pocket money + 3p
*or* $y = 2\,(x) + 3$.

We can also show the relationship as two sets of figures or pairs of co-ordinates, from which we can plot the graph:

| Fred's pocket money | Hilda's pocket money |
|---|---|
| 10p | 23p |
| 20p | 43p |
| 30p | 63p |

(*iii*) Sometimes children can be given 'sums' in the form of a grid in which the top line of numbers all have the same rule (function) applied to them and thus produce the numbers in the bottom line. The answers to all these sums can be read off a graph drawn using the top line as the *x* co-ordinates (the domain of the function) and the bottom line as the *y* co-ordinates (the target of the function). Thus, from the graph, the answers can be filled in the boxes (Figure 9).

| 4 | 0 | 1 | 7 | 10 | | |
|---|---|---|---|---|---|---|
| ↓ | ↓ | ↓ | ↓ | ↓ | ↓ | ↓ |
| 6 | −2 | 0 | | | 10 | 8 |

Figure 9

(*iv*) More complex function graphs usually belong in the secondary school but some primary children can experiment by drawing graphs of square numbers and cubic numbers. The triangular numbers can also be graphed. This will encourage children to make a connection between graphical work and the number work they have done earlier on.

It is always important to emphasize the inter-connectedness of all the various different topic areas in mathematics, especially to children who are sometimes taught as if each topic were in a separate box isolated from and unconnected to the rest of the subject.

## Other types of graphs using co-ordinates

There are many sorts of graph, other than relationship or function graphs, which rely on co-ordinates. Indeed, most graphs do so to some extent. These different types of graphical and pictorial representation are covered in chapter 14.

# 14

# Pictorial representation

## Different types of pictorial representation

There are so many ways of displaying information that it is possible to feel intimidated by the welter of block graphs, scatter graphs, histograms, piecharts, and so on, that figure in any maths education textbook. It is important to remember, however, that a graph or diagram is only helpful if it makes something clearer, or is a way of finding an answer to a problem.

The first point to convey, therefore, is the purpose of the representation. It is never appropriate to set up a plan or activity with the sole purpose of drawing a block graph. The representation of information is the end point of an activity and not the start of it and the information or data collected will itself play a role in deciding the appropriate way to display it. Thus a block graph can sometimes be the simplest method of displaying data clearly for children, but not always. Suppose the children are doing a project on transport and are considering the different methods of transport used to come to school. They do a survey and discover that out of 30 children in the class, 25 walk, 1 comes by bus, 1 by car, 1 by train and 2 cycle. A block graph would not, given the data, be a sensible way to display the information, for it would consist of one extremely tall column and a thin line of blocks along the $x$ axis. The data would be better displayed on a Venn diagram.

So the nature and quality of the information together with the purpose of the survey or investigation will be crucial factors when deciding on the appropriate type of pictorial representation.

(*i*) Block graphs. These are very commonly used in schools, sometimes inappropriately. However they remain a very practical and immediate way of displaying information, especially in the infant school, because each child can colour their own block on the graph.

A good example of an exercise involving the production of a block graph is a survey of the most watched television programmes. Children list the programmes they each watch regularly (there may be some dispute about what counts as regularly!), and a tally is made of the 12 most popular programmes. These are then represented on a block graph. It is worth noting that some children's names may appear more than once on the graph whilst other names may not appear at all. The information collected and displayed says something about the children, but its main purpose is to consider the popularity of the programmes (Figure 1).

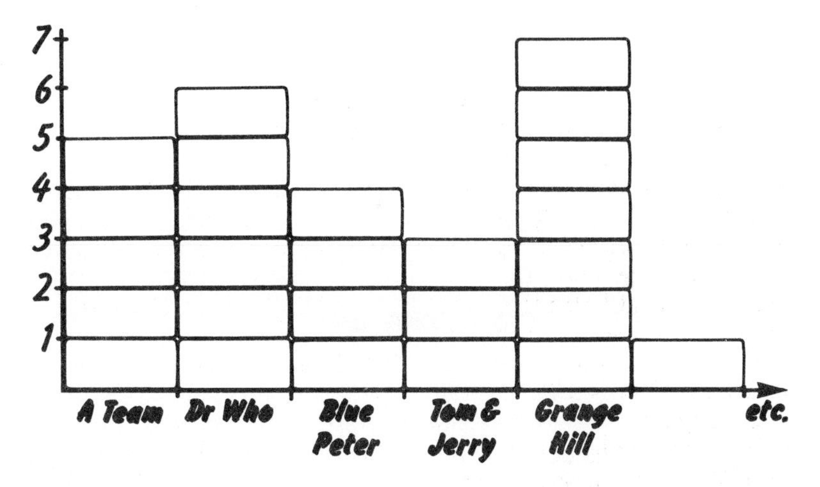


Figure 1

A second suggestion for data appropriately depicted on a block graph is the results of a survey on the months or days the children were born. On this graph each child appears once and only once. In both these graphs there is no relationship at all between one column and the next: because 4 children were born in September it does not mean that there will be 5 in October and 6 in November. Also, if a new child comes into the class it is not possible to predict by looking at the graph in which month their birthday will fall.

(*ii*) Comparison graphs. Sometimes it is necessary to depict information in such a way that a comparison is made clear. For example we may want to compare all the children's handspans. To compare them we might lay them in a long line from tallest to shortest (Figure 2). This is a way of displaying the handspans and of demonstrating the relationship between them, and is sometimes referred to as a 'strip graph'. Similarly a comparative graph could be drawn to show shoe sizes, or foot lengths, in the class.

A block graph could be made comparing how many letters there are in the children's names.

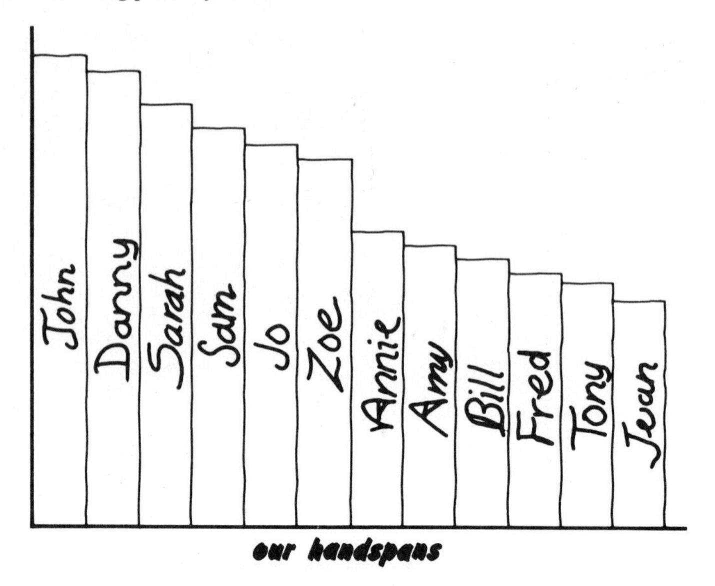


Figure 2

(*iii*) Bar charts. In a bar chart the blocks used in a block graph are replaced by a continuous bar. For example the number of pints of milk taken a day by the families represented in the class can be charted as shown (Figure 3). The frequency or 'count' is represented by a bar, so the longest bar represents the number of pints most frequently taken.

(*iv*) Histograms. 'Histogram' is a technical term not ideally suited for use in the primary classroom, but a histogram can be thought of as an extension of a bar chart where the area of each rectangle represents the frequency. Thus in Figure 4 the highest rectangle represents the amount of pocket money most frequently obtained.

(*v*) Venn diagrams. On occasion, the fact that one child's name might appear three times in a block graph may render that graph confusing and it might be better to seek other ways of displaying the information gathered. In such cases a Venn diagram has considerable advantages because it displays visually the relationships between sets of objects. If we have information about sets of children and sets of things which are inter-related in some way then a Venn diagram is often the most suitable form of representation. In the example of the television programmes watched by the class, mentioned earlier a Venn diagram would possibly be more suitable than a block graph. Another example might be a survey of pets kept by the

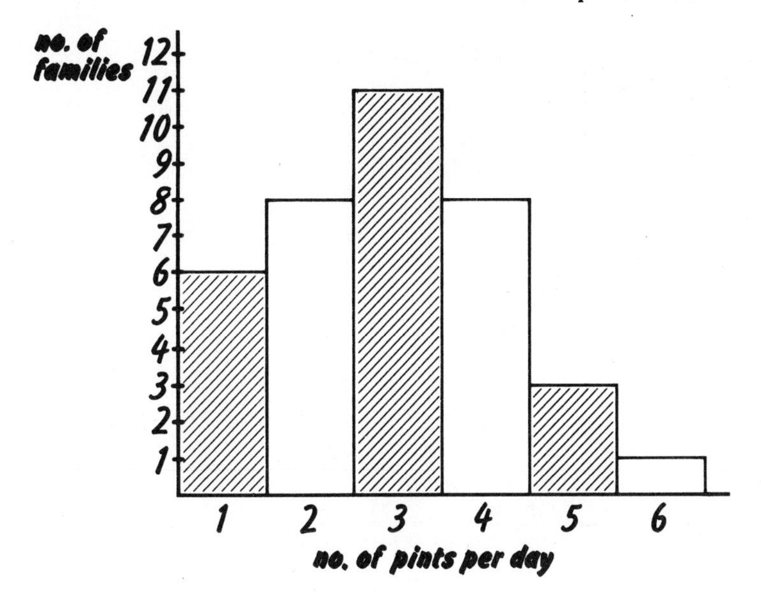


Figure 3

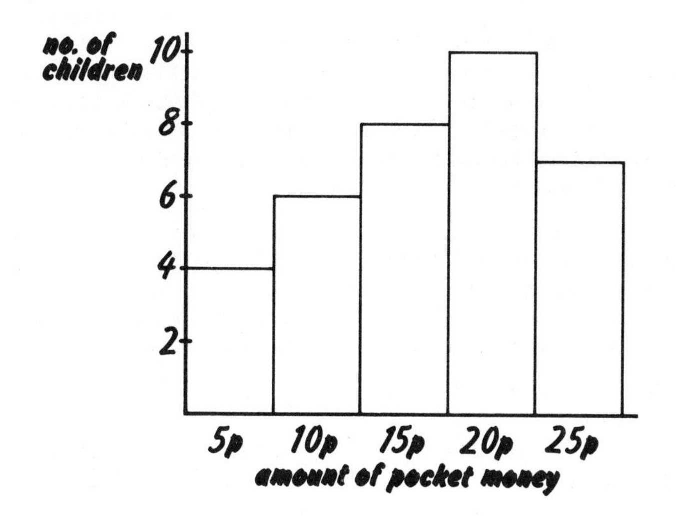


Figure 4

children. A Venn diagram of the results of their survey might look like this (Figure 5).
Each child's name appears only once on the diagram and yet it is perfectly possible to obtain from the diagram all the information,

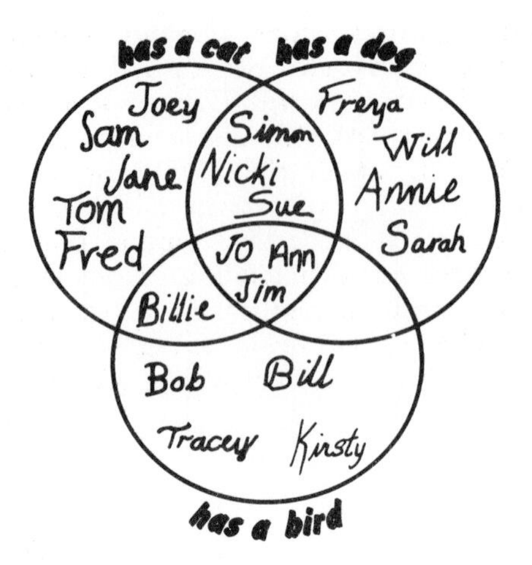


Figure 5

and more, which could be obtained from a block graph. It is clear from the Venn diagram that 12 children own cats which, in this class, are the most popular pets. It is also clear that of those 12 children, 7 own other pets as well as a cat. This information is not immediately obtainable from the block graph. It is clear from the diagram that no child owns only a dog and a bird, once again, information not easily available from the graph. Furthermore, it is possible to ascertain from the diagram that there are 20 children in the class who have pets. In this example, because we are concerned with the relationship between sets of children, the Venn diagram provides much more effective representation than the block graph.

(*vi*) Conversion graphs. It is not required, or even advisable, for children to convert one thing into another very often during primary school. Inches and centimetres, kilometres and miles, and so on, are seen and taught as separate units of measure and children are encouraged to move comfortably from one to the other, to be able to work easily in both, without ever having to convert one into the other. Conversion of measures, metres and centimetres into feet and inches, for example, is usually performed when a person cannot 'think' in metres and so has to convert everything into the unit in which they can work.

Nowadays, importance is laid on establishing the whole concept of measurement and of a repeated unit; consequently, most children should be able to move quite happily from measuring in one unit to measuring in another so there is much less need for conversion charts. However, there are occasions when it is most useful to be able to convert one thing into another. The most common situation in which this occurs is when on holiday abroad. If a person is staying only a week or two in a country with a different currency they do not have time to become sufficiently accustomed to that currency to think and work in it. Under these circumstances being able to convert fast and efficiently is very useful. Children can draw conversion graphs which help them do this. Suppose that at a certain time the number of French francs obtainable for £1 sterling is 11. Using this information a graph can be drawn which will enable us to read off any amount in francs and see immediately how much it is worth in £s. The following pairs of co-ordinates are plotted to draw the graph (Figure 6):

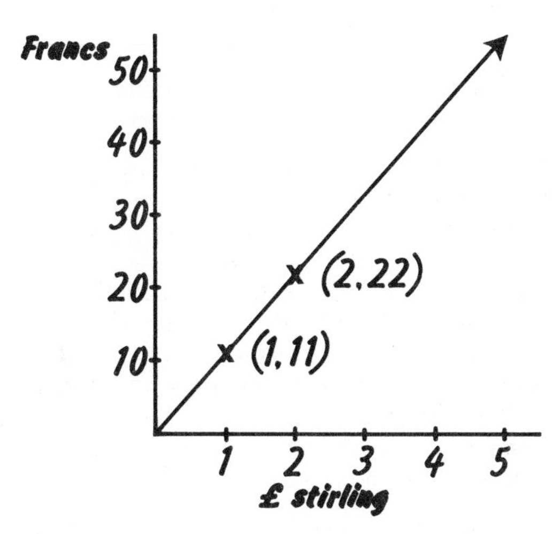


Figure 6

£1 = 11f
£5 = 55f
£10 = 110f

(*vii*) Pie charts. Pie charts display the relative proportions of each part of the data collected. They are a particularly useful means of display when these proportions are what we want to know about. For example, if children are calculating how much time each day is spent on various activities, sleeping, eating, playing, working, watching TV and so on, then a pie chart will show the proportion of each day spent on each activity (Figure 7).

Figure 7

Sometimes pie charts are used to demonstrate the proportions of a particular institution's expenditure which go to pay for different things. Children can make their own pie charts to show the spending pattern of their own yearly income. They will have to consider carefully the categories under which to place the various amounts spent: for example, do they have a separate category marked 'comics' or do comics count as 'books' for the purposes of the pie chart?

(*viii*) Self creating graphs. Sometimes there are activities which form a kind of graph by virtue of the kind of activity they are. If the viscosity or stickiness of different fluids is being tested, a drop of each fluid, milk, water, fruit juice, syrup, etc., can be placed at intervals on the $x$ axis and the radius of the spread will form the graph. Similarly, if candles are lined up and lit, then one is blown out every 10 minutes and the candles left standing, they form a graph which shows the rate of burning (Figure 8).

(*ix*) Scatter graphs. These are graphs which show two pieces of information about children in the class, or about each object in a set, at the same time. For example, foot size can be plotted against handspan for each member of the class (Figure 9). The randomness of organization of the scatter will give a clue as to whether any relationship exists between these two things. Other examples of scatter graphs include plotting reach (length from finger-tip to finger-tip with arms outstretched) against height, and age against weight.

(*x*) 3-dimensional graphs. 3-dimensional graphs can be created as an alternative to either a scatter graph or a Venn diagram where

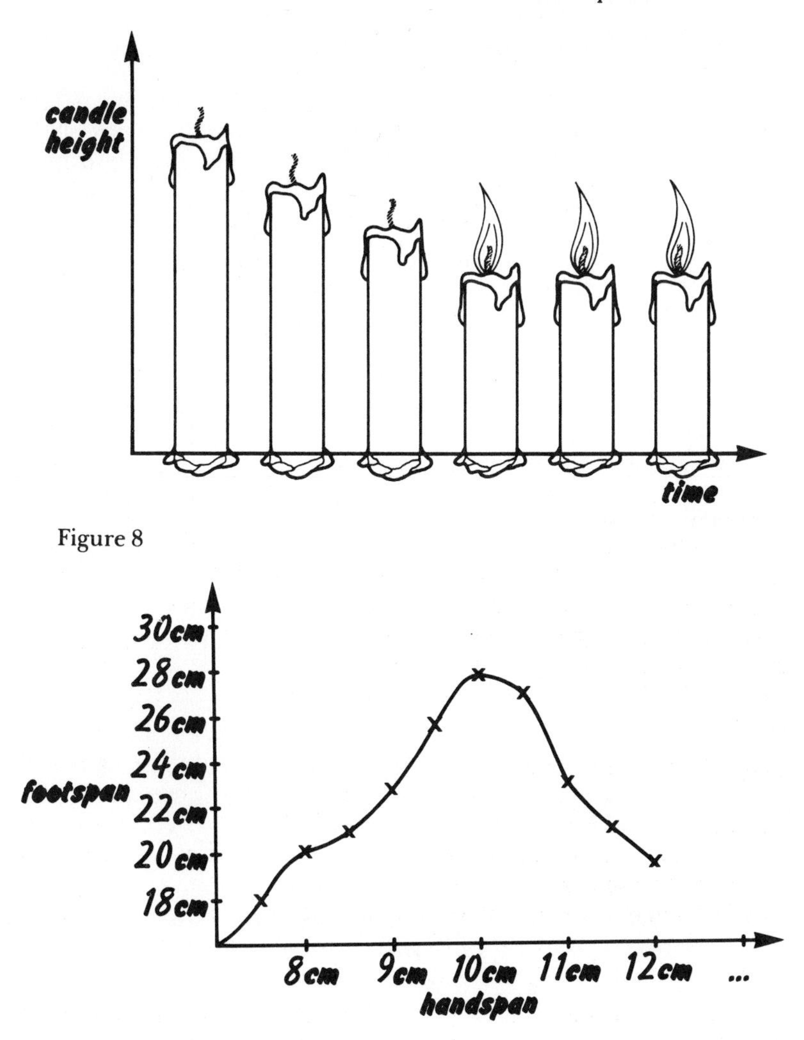


Figure 8

Figure 9

more than two relationships are involved. An example would be a graph representing which children in the class have brothers or sisters.

(*xi*) Relationship or function graphs. These graphs show in pictorial form the relationship between one variable and another, as in a tables graph. They have been dealt with in chapter 13.

## Collecting and sorting data

The collection and organization of information is as much a part of producing a graph as the drawing of the axes and the making of the blocks. A graph conveys information and that information must have been collected and organized before it could be displayed on a graph.

(*i*) Categorization. Deciding what headings are necessary is often one of the most difficult parts of collecting the information. When doing a traffic survey outside the school gates, for example, children must decide what vehicles to count under which headings. Are vans to be counted as 'lorries' or separately? Do ambulances have a category of their own or do they come under some wider group such as 'emergency vehicles'? The answers to these questions and the decisions made about the headings to be used will, in part, depend upon the expected nature of the information being collected. For example, if the school happens to be round the corner from an ambulance station it is probably worth having ambulances as a separate category.

The way the information is sorted and then classified affects not only the appearance of the graph but, in some cases the data itself. For example, if vans and cars are put into one category, two things may happen: large vans may be classified as lorries which might mean that the graph gave a misleading reading on how many lorries passed the school; and the children will not record the number of vans passing the school so that information will not simply be masked but will not be there at all.

(*ii*) Counting and tallying. Children have to be able to get down their information quickly and efficiently and in such a way that they can read what it says afterwards. In the case of the traffic survey, this may well involve the children in two useful techniques – group work and tallying. It is obviously not efficient for each child to count everything in all categories, therefore the collection of data can be split up and different parts of the task carried out by different children – one child, or pair of children, can count vans, another cars, a third lorries, etc. This will minimize the possibility of error and assist in maintaining a reasonable standard of accuracy. The children make a tally of the numbers of vehicles as they count them.

Sometimes the collection of data will not depend on accurate counting or tallying but rather upon good organization of the information. So if everyone is being asked what their favourite animals are, the children will have to think of a way of taking down the information under certain expected headings in such a way as to leave open the possibility of adding new categories as the survey continues. For example, the children might start by asking each child what animals they like and obtain a list which looks like Figure 10. Alternatively, they might start with a list looking like Figure 11, which could produce different results since the suggested headings may trigger certain responses.

Children also learn that neatness and precision actually matter when collecting and recording data and often improve in these areas accordingly.

Joey - cat, dog, sloth, pig
Annie - mouse, rabbit, dog
Sally - monkey, cat, lion
Sam - hedgehog, mouse, squirrel, cat

and so on

Figure 10

| cats | dogs | mice | pigs | etc. |
|---|---|---|---|---|
| ✓ | ✓ | ✓ | ✓ | |
| ✓ | ✓ | | | |
| ✓ | | | | |
| ✓ | | | | |

Figure 11

**Averages**

There are so many ways of producing averages that it is hard to know what is meant when the word 'average' is used. It is important that children realize that there is more than one method of finding a figure for an average so that they are able to develop critical judgements about statistics they read or are given on television.

(*i*) Average – arithmetic mean. This is perhaps the most common method used to find an average and at one time it was the only one taught in primary schools. If there are 30 children in the class their average age can be calculated by adding up all their ages and dividing by 30. This method produces the 'arithmetic mean' of their ages. The method has one big disadvantage as a way of finding an average and that is that freak statistics may disproportionately affect the average. So, if there are 10 children in a group and their pocket money figures are: 50p, 45p. 35p, 30p, 50p, 35p, 45p, 40p, 50p, 500p, then the average pocket money calculated using this algorithm will be 88p. This is obviously not the average amount of pocket money received but is inflated because of the £5 given to one lucky individual. Freak results can render this method fairly useless, though it may be appropriate for calculating the average age of the class where the ages range from 8.6 years to 9.5 years.

*(ii)* Mode. This is sometimes called 'the shopkeepers' average'. If the teacher decides to sell biscuits to the children at the school jumble sale, s/he may decide, for practical reasons, that s/he can only sell one variety. So the children conduct a survey to find out which biscuits are most popular, and produce the following graph (Figure 12). According to the graph, 11 children liked chocolate fingers and this proved to be the biscuit liked by the largest number of children. This, then, is the biscuit liked most on average. In a situation like this there is no point in using the method given earlier because finally only one item can be chosen. But the mode can also be useful in finding an average even if it is possible to find the mean. Suppose the results of a test in a class were that 15 children got 16 out of 20, 3 got 17, 2 got 15 and 4 got 3 out of 20. The mode will be 16, whereas the mean will be about 14. In this case the mode gives us a more reasonable idea as to what was the average result achieved.

*(iii)* The median is the figure obtained when the results at either edge of the graph are checked off against each other until the mid-point of all the results is arrived at. If the sizes of shoe in the class are: 5, 3, 2, 2, 1, 1, 1, 1, 13, 13, 13, 12, 12, 12, 12, 12, 11, 11, 10, 10, 9, the median is the figure arrived at by counting in from the edges until the middle is reached. In this case it is 13 whereas the mode is 12. The mean is impossible to calculate since shoe sizes go from 13 to 1 which would make a nonsense of the arithmetic.

## Use of the computer for information retrieval and data processing

There are microcomputer information handling systems now available that allow children to record the results of their own surveys on disc and then give them access to this information through the use of text, diagrams, graphs and charts. Some of the information handling systems are more suitable than others for primary-age children in the types of recording they allow and the sorts of information they

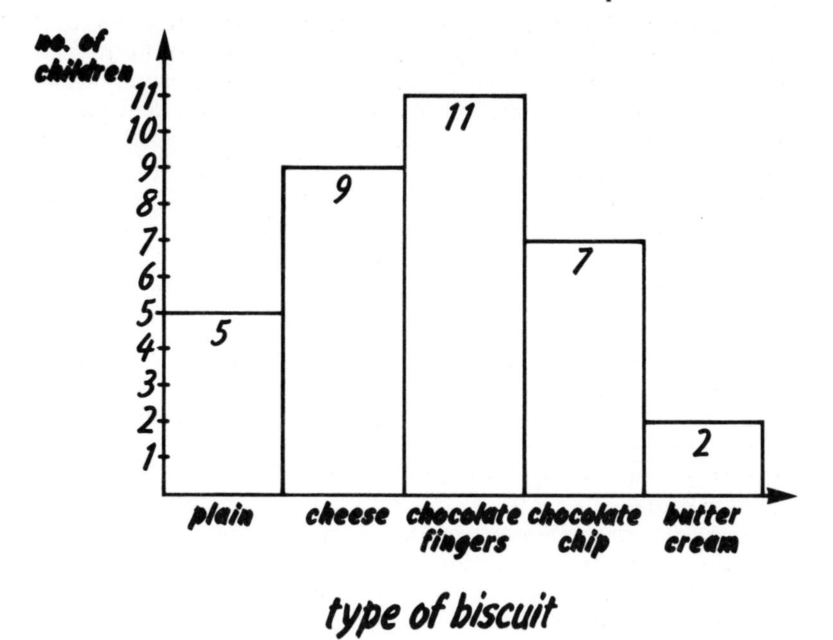


Figure 12

generate. Sometimes the process of feeding information into such filing systems is a tedious one, involving long lists of co-ordinates and figures, but it is not a difficult task and can be shared out amongst a group of children.

It is important that children learn to operate data files and become familiar with the use of the microcomputer in the field of information retrieval, if only because it is an area in which computers are likely to be increasingly used. But many of the same problems of collecting and sorting information, of classification and deciding about headings will still arise whether or not the information is to be handled and presented by a child or a computer.

# 15

# Conclusion

Throughout the book there has been an emphasis on two things:

1) Adopting a problem-solving approach to the teaching of mathematics.
2) The importance of practical activities in developing mathematical understanding.

Certain very practical organizational questions are raised by these assumptions:

(*i*) Involving children in a large number of activities of this nature will inevitably mean a more or less integrated approach to the subject. This is because 'problems' seldom fall neatly within the 'subject' boundaries. For example, a class or group of children were set the following problem: *Construct a parachute such that it will, when thrown or dropped out of a top floor window, carry an egg (not hard-boiled!) down to the ground and deposit it unbroken.*

These children were given particular materials to work with – plastic sheeting, fabric, paper, string, glue, sellotape, masking tape, cotton thread, paper cups, etc. They were also asked to work in groups of two or three and a prize was offered to the group which produced the parachute with the slowest descent! The children timed their various trial descents and recorded their information upon a computer in a data file. (However, they could have recorded this without the computer, if necessary.)

The mathematics involved in this problem is extensive. The children used: sorting, classifying and displaying of data; measurement in length, area, time, weight, speed; shape and symmetry; and finally a great deal of numerical calculation involving things like differences, averages and ratio. All these mathematical topics were embedded within a particular context which meant that the children tackled each problem as it arose and with a strong motivation for getting an answer. The co-operative approach meant that quite a lot of peer-group learning went on and some of the explanations and arguments which took place between the children themselves were crucial to the acquisition of particular mathematical skills.

To teach mathematics at least partly in this way does make certain organizational assumptions. It assumes a classroom where the children can work in groups and become experienced at so doing. Some children, especially juniors for whom this is a novel idea, take a while to settle to group work, and the teacher has to persevere and work hard to help the children gain some of the co-operative learning skills – the ability to listen to others, to lead without bossing, to make suggestions and take criticism, and then to corporately apportion the work to be done in an equable and equal fashion.

This type of work also assumes that the teacher has the timetable flexibility to allow children whole 'lumps' of time when they can work consistently on this project. When one is involved in trying to solve a problem, it is essential to be given time to sort out particular problems as and when they arise. Otherwise, the whole attempt at problem-solving may become frustrating in the extreme. So, there is an assumption of a certain degree of timetable fiexibility within the school day, if not an integrated day.

The use of a problem-solving approach does rely quite heavily upon very careful and accurate record-keeping. Some children may 'opt out' of mathematics and slide into the role of recorder rather than active participator. The teacher needs to be aware what each child has done in terms of their personal involvement in the mathematics intrinsic to the problem-solving process. As well as individual records, the teacher also needs a record of what the whole activity involved in terms of the mathematics covered. In this way, if the children have done two projects which required the same sort of mathematics in both, then a problem requiring that the children branch out and try something new can be set. The sorts of individual and class records which a teacher has to keep under these circumstances are very different from those which are kept, for example, by any teacher relying totally upon the children in the class working page by page through a commercial mathematics scheme. However, once a system for individual record-keeping, plus of course, class record-keeping, has been devised, it should not take much longer than the old-fashioned commercial mathematics records.

(*ii*) Involving the use of practical activities at all levels and at all times in the learning of mathematics will have automatic implications in the field of resources. The structural apparatus needs to be visible, and put where it can be easily obtained by the child of whatever age. The more difficult access to practical apparatus is made by circumstances, the less children (and teachers!) will be inclined to use it. Also, children need to see structural apparatus, including calculators, as a part of normal mathematical work, and not as something which 'is only got out if you can't do it without'.

A classroom in which the use of structural apparatus is taken for granted and in which mathematics is approached practically at all levels is unlikely to be a permanently quiet and 'sitting at desks' classroom. Mathematics lessons will inevitably involve children getting up, looking for things to assist them in their work, doing things rather than only writing them. This asks for a greater tolerance on the part of the teacher for a certain amount of 'structured disorder'! This is not to say that practical mathematics leads to chaos – far from it. But it may be necessary to realize that sitting down and quietly working in a book is not going to be synonomous with a good mathematics lesson.

(*iii*) The type of approach advocated by the Cockcroft Report, echoed by the HMI Document and reinforced throughout this book is not, by and large, one which parents share. This is partly, I believe, the fault of the teaching profession – teachers, as well as, inspectors, advisors, and HMIs. However, it is also true that changing people's attitudes to and perceptions of a subject is notoriously difficult and it takes time. It is essential that, as teachers, we take account of parental feelings in this matter. Parents have, at the very least, a right to be concerned in the matter of their children's education. They are often anxious about the subject of mathematics themselves, having all too frequently failed it at school. Therefore, any contact with the parents in this field – offering workshops on maths, getting parents into the classroom to do some maths with their children, allowing children to take maths home with them (and I do not mean pages of sums!) – all these things can help to allay parental anxiety and show them that the mathematics their children are being taught will fit them for their future lives.

What this book is really about is the passing on, through activities, through games, through playing, and through all the means at our disposal, of a love for, and an appreciation of, mathematics. Unless we enjoy the subject ourselves, we stand no chance of convincing anyone else to do so. Maths is too important and is too much fun to be left with the dusty and boring image it seems to have acquired. Today's teachers are helping to change that image for good.

# Bibliography


Bruner, J. *Towards a Theory of Instruction*, Cambridge, Mass., 1967.

Bruner, J. *The Process of Education* Harvard,

Bryant, P. *Perception and Understanding in Young Children*; Methuen, 1974.

Burton, L. *Thinking Things Through*, Basil Blackwell, 1984.

Denvir, Stolz, Brown. *Low Attainers in Mathematics 5–16*, Methuen Educational, 1982.

Dickson, Brown, Gibson. *Children Learning Mathematics* Holt Educational, 1984.

Donaldson, M. *Childrens' Minds*, Fontana, 1978.

Floyd, A. *Developing Mathematical Thinking*, Addison-Wesley, 1981.

Hart, K. *Children's Understanding of Mathematics: 11–16*, John Murray, 1981.

HMI Cockcroft Report, *Mathematics Counts*, 1982.

HMI Curriculum Matters No. 3, *Mathematics from 5–16*, 1985.

Howson, Keital, Kilpatrick. *Curriculum Development in Mathematics*, C.U.P.

Hughes, M. *Children and Number*, Basil Blackwell, 1986.

Ginsburg, H. *Children's Arithmetic: How They Learn It and How You Teach It*, Austin, 1982.

Langdon, N. and Snape, C. *A Way with Maths*, Cambridge, 1985.

Mottershead, L. *Souces of Mathematical Discovery*, Basil Blackwell, 1984.

Mottershead, L. *Investigations in Mathematics* Basil Blackwell, 1985.

Paling, D. *Teaching Mathematics in a Primary School*, O.U.P.

Schools Council Curriculum Bulletin No. 1, *Mathematics in Primary Schools*, HMSO, 1972.

Shuard, H. and Rothery, A. *Children Reading Mathematics*, John Murray, 1980.

Skemp, R. *The Psychology of Learning Mathematics*, Penguin

Williams, E. and Shuard, H. *Primary Mathematics Today*, Longman, 1982 ed.